nobody remembers the birdman

NEW WRITING SCOTLAND 40

Edited by
Rachelle Atalla
and
Marjorie Lotfi

Gaelic editor:
Maggie Rabatski

Association for Scottish Literature

Association for Scottish Literature
Scottish Literature, 7 University Gardens
University of Glasgow, Glasgow G12 8QH
www.asls.org.uk

ASL is a registered charity no. SC006535

First published 2022

British Library Cataloguing in Publication Data

A CIP record for this book is available
from the British Library

ISBN 978-1-906841-48-5

The Association for Scottish Literature
acknowledges the support of Creative Scotland
towards the publication of this book

Typeset in Minion by ASL
Printed by Ashford Colour Press, Gosport

CONTENTS

INTRODUCTION

Here we are, at the tail end of a global pandemic, wondering, what comes next? How do we return to a world that is utterly changed? What is the role of writing as we emerge into a daily life at once unfamiliar and yet vaguely or (even worse instantly) recognisable? We are forever changed by the events of the past two years – whether it's the loss of loved ones, illness, or the profound disconnect from the people around us, a real change in the way we live our daily lives. What stories, what images in words, will help us recover and find our rhythm again?

For this issue, we chose from over six hundred submissions, many of them containing more than one piece, and each with a distinct voice and story to tell. As an editor, it's a real privilege to read the work of so many of your fellow writers, and to carry it in your imagination over time. The stories and poems in this volume are the ones that stayed with us in the weeks between our readings. Our conversations about selection involved laughter, curiosity, and the genuine sense that we'd both been moved by so many of the submissions. The selection in this volume contains storms and satellites, homecomings and memories of home, losses and discoveries, and words that literally break open and then settle across the page.

Though unintentional, the pieces we chose often point out our failings while reminding us that kindness prevails, that despite our enforced disconnect, real human connection is possible: the hand on the back, the first 'I love you' years later than expected, the community that finally (too late?) accepts an incomer as their own. Neighbours just out of sight mirror our actions, articulate how we think about and empathise with the people we often can't even see.

Without setting out to, we chose pieces that suggest how we move forward, how we might already hold in ourselves what we need to begin to repair what we've lost in these years. The title poem 'nobody remembers the birdman' reminds us both that we carry those we lose with us, and that the man moving forward both brings his whole self to this new life, and simultaneously carries his 'house on his back / feathers falling from beneath his coat.' Other pieces suggest we build a new version of ourselves; as Karen Elizabeth Bishop reminds us in 'cairn', put simply, 'we rise.'

The fisherman in the first piece in this *New Writing Scotland* 40 stands between two nations, two places, focussed on his task despite the water shifting around him. It seems fitting, somehow, that this first poem that places us between things, carrying on, and reminds us the natural world around us continues much as it always has, that as ever, the 'river braids intae sea'. So many of the poems chosen examine home, and a sense of belonging: Shehzar Doja gives us a language for loss in his 'A sequence of loss', while Roshni Gallagher, in 'My Granny Dreams of Guyana', tells us that 'things change', that we should 'pull quiet in to cover us.' Lynn Davidson's 'From Scotland to New Zealand' gives us a vision of arriving back home to the familiar after a long journey 'recovering from this // long breath-held dive to get here. / The shudder of relief'.

There is much to interpret from the pieces of prose selected, each in their own way reflecting on the world in which we live. With the current cost-of-living crisis looming, Hannah McDonald's 'Jam and Butter' is a poignant story told from a child's perspective, contemplating the realities of poverty, while in contrast Callum McSorley's 'The Last Good Thing' is a powerful speculative tale of excessiveness, hinting perhaps at our capitalist appetites never being fully satisfied. Jane Archer's 'Phenomenal Waves' captures a haunting sense of waiting for the inevitable, so much out of our control, while Niki Brennan's 'Gather' aches with loss, grief and disconnection.

The quality of work we receive continues to astound us. It is a joy to edit these anthologies and we're delighted to be publishing these truly talented writers in our special fortieth issue. Rachelle's tenure at *New Writing Scotland* is coming to an end and she will be sad to leave, but it is time to hand over the baton and welcome a new co-editor on board. As always, thank you to all those who submit and trust us with their work; to the tirelessly hardworking team in the ASL office, Duncan Jones and Pip Osmond-Williams; as well as to our very talented cover designer, Mark Mechan.

We hope you enjoy *New Writing Scotland* 40.

Marjorie and Rachelle

NEW WRITING SCOTLAND 41:
SUBMISSION INSTRUCTIONS

The forty-first volume of *New Writing Scotland* will be published in summer 2023. Submissions are invited from writers resident in Scotland or Scots by birth, upbringing or inclination. All forms of writing are welcome: autobiography and memoirs; creative responses to events and experiences; drama; graphic artwork (monochrome only); poetry; political and cultural commentary and satire; short fiction; travel writing or any other creative prose may be submitted, but not full-length plays or novels, though self-contained extracts are acceptable. The work must not be previously published or accepted for publication elsewhere, and may be in any of the languages of Scotland.

Submissions should be uploaded, for free, via Submittable:

nws.submittable.com/submit

Prose pieces should be double-spaced and carry an approximate word-count. Please do not put your name on your submission; instead, please provide your name and contact details, including email and postal addresses, on a covering letter. If you are sending more than one piece, please group everything into one document. **Please send no more than four poems, or one prose work.**

Authors retain all rights to their work(s) and are free to submit and/or publish the same work(s) elsewhere after they appear in *New Writing Scotland*. Successful contributors will be paid at a rate of £25 per published page.

Please be aware that we have limited space in each edition, and therefore shorter pieces are more suitable – although longer items of exceptional quality may still be included. Our maximum suggested word-count is 3,500 words, and the submission deadline is **Monday 31 October 2022.**

Craig Aitchison
FISHIN THE MAIRCH

The mairch haiks seawart. In watter's
mid, atween twa nations, the angler
kevels, steids ilka fit, casts. He flisks
awa fashin thouchts – faimly, finance,
wark's wirries. Slicht skite ae soles on roond,
slakit stanes, till bait rests oan smaw watter.
Inklin lippers dwyne. He's paised noo.

In gled watter, a saumon – siller arrae
specklet wi glog – slidders by lure an soe
flindrikin. Browden, door, thrawn fish.
North Sea miles ahint, aheid strics tae loup,
lips, boonds an mairches tae shrug aff.

Tweed Watter scrauchles East, until flowe dunts
bore, fresh meets saut, river braids intae sea.

Juliet Antill
USES OF A COMPASS

Me and Lorna Clarke scuffed our t-bars
at the bus-stop; we sucked
on Fishermen's Friends, rubbed ink
off our hands with peppery spit.

We knew the point of a pistil,
the patterns of Alpine transhumance,
that Lima was the capital of Peru;
we were hazy on *savoir* v. *connaître*.

Once a man we knew – or thought
we knew – picked us up. *Quicker than the bus,*
he said. He smiled too much
and looked at our knees.

What we wanted was to be fifteen,
to scratch NORTHERN SOUL
on our school-bags
and know where Wigan was.

Jane Archer
PHENOMENAL WAVES

The dog appeared a couple of weeks before the storm. My home was on short stilts and the stringy beast crawled underneath to sleep, often whining. I thought that it still lived with the expectation of a boot up the backside; but the coat was soft, and there were no welts, no dark furless scars. It kept sniffing the air, receiving messages from the breeze. In the mornings, I shooed him away; but he sat under a nearby tree, licking his paws, sneezing regularly with patches of sand stuck to a damp nose, and staring out to sea.

I lived on a beach scattered with shells. They were tiny and translucent like a baby's fingernails. If you crouched down, lowered your face to the sand, the shell would hitch up, hair-like legs appear, and march off sideways. It's a strange thing to see something that shouldn't move get up and walk; it's as if a tree coughed or a flower yawned. I spent mornings trying not to stand on them as I made my way to the tree, which stood between my house and the water. I hung washing while keeping one eye on the ground for movement. The sand-crabs carried their home wherever they went.

While the sand-crabs looked unperturbed, the edgy dog wasn't the only one that figured the storm's arrival. The air no longer carried the sweet scent of woodsmoke; instead, a sharp salty wind nipped the nose and throat. The world lost ease with itself as birds disappeared from the sky and trees bowed lofty heads. On my way to get groceries, I stepped over escaped rubbish to get to the shop. Martha was at the counter as usual.

'Hey,' she said, without smiling. 'What you wantin?' This surly attitude was not a sign of badness as Martha never felt the need to pretend she liked people.

I was careful not to buy too much as everything was more expensive than in town. I told her what I was after.

'Not wantin my pasties?'

'No, thanks,' I said.

She clicked her tongue as she moved her bulk around the shop. 'Noticed the light's been switched on in the tower,' she said. 'Tellin us all there's somethin on its way.'

I picked up a bottle of red wine and Martha looked at me.

'Plentee drinkin,' she said as she handed over my change. I could tell she watched me as I left the shop.

On the way back the wind was gusting up the back of my skirt, blowing hair in my face. There was anger in it. As I went up the steps to the house I saw the dog skulking under the balcony, eyes big as plates staring out to sea.

'What you seeing, boy?' I said.

He paid no attention other than to creep around in circles, tightening himself into a ball with his tail coiled over his backside and through his legs.

'You a bit frightened then? You and me both.'

At the door, I saw a ragged piece of paper strapped under a rock, sitting on the edge of the balcony. It was from the woman who owned the house. And in scrawled writing it said:

Sorry not to see you. There has been a storm warning and you must leave the house.

I went inside and looked out the window. Old Colonel, who lived a short distance from the back of the house, was patching up his cottage. His glassy eyes were still able to direct the hammer to nail and he worked swiftly. We rarely spoke. He would nod in passing but his interests didn't include talking. He preferred the canaries that flew around his house and an idle goat that seemed to produce nothing other than the odd shit. I put the radio on. It was official, a storm was to come to the island. The radio-man announced the possible wind-strength and height of waves; he called them phenomenal waves.

The radio-man announced the shelters in different parts of the island and I started to pack my things. Living on my own had made me awkward about staying with others. Somehow, I acted in a different way: often too polite, eating food I didn't want, asking questions with no real interest in the answer. And sleeping was such a private thing, as was going to the bathroom. The ease and simplicity of these things became complicated and embarrassing in the company of others. They needed to be timed and checked out. It was not that I didn't like people; I had just lost my way in how to live with them. Strange how these things change. Not so long ago I didn't think twice as I barely had time to think the first time round. Work and a woman made me rarely worry about being with other people, or myself for that matter. But change creeps up whether you've got a job and an arm around your waist or not. Change comes looking for you whether you want it or not. And, with these thoughts in mind, I put the packed bag down and decided to stay.

*

I locked the door and lit the lamp on the table. Before long I boarded up the windows as each sound in the house got louder. Footsteps echoed when I moved in the room. When the wind found violence, I breathed in time to its beat against the door. I decided it was time for alcohol. The first glass went down well: warm and sweet. I drank more. The heat in the room intensified. I kept my clothes on as I lay in bed. The lamp cast shadows of devils across the room. A print of Madonna and Child twitched in the light; the child suckled hard, and the mother stroked the hair of the baby. A large spider did a gravity-defying scamper over the ceiling and grew larger as it moved. In the haze, a stranger with furrowed brow and unbreakable stare appeared. Oil-black hair was thrown over her shoulders, down her almighty back. She mouthed words I couldn't make out. Banners were cradled in her middle, reaching up to the vaulted ceiling above. She smiled, encouraging me to read the signs of danger. Great rolls of robe were swept aside as she turned, moving away, leaving me. And I thought of the woman I once lived with, thought of her leaving, thought of the brick I wanted to break over the heads of friends who told me I was better off without her. It never occurred to me that I would end up living alone. But she left, and I moved to the island.

I thought I heard the dog, but the wind hammered any noise away. It was as if the sea had separated itself from the world; no longer my companion, it was searching, hammering around the house. The door began to bend as wind and water hit thin wood. It stood up to the beating but there was something in its creaks and groans that told me it would give in. I pulled up the sheet, gathering it around my shoulders. The window let out a shrieking scream, and along with a crash came the sound of a waterfall; light poured through broken glass. One of the shutters had been ripped off. The bright eye of the moon threw a spotlight on an enormous grey ogre growing out of the water until it stood on its hind legs. It was still for several seconds before free-falling on the house. The water plummeted through the window.

A voice spoke from the water. 'Is anyone in there?' it said.

'I am.'

More glass shattered and a louder voice said: 'Hello?'

I turned to see the door hammered down in one movement. The sea gushed in and two men stood knee-deep in water. 'Let's get you out of here,' said a man with a tight mouth.

I scrabbled towards them. 'What about the dog? He's under the house.'

The other younger man, whose body had not quite grown into his head, pointed at me.

'We're not here for a dog. We need to get you to a safe place.'

*

The next morning, it was as if someone had used a machine-gun on the trees, as they lay flat on their backs. The Colonel's cottage had leapt in the air and landed in a crumpled heap in the same place; but I couldn't see the house I lived in. Walls and doors and windows and ceiling were gone. The lone toilet, no longer attached to plumbing, sat looking vulnerable and exposed without the privacy of a small room. I was embarrassed, even though the walls hadn't disappeared while I was on it. And behind it, the sea had been turned inside out. It made sense that if a wave was strong enough to suck in a whole house, then it was strong enough to get its fingers deep underneath the reef and uproot it in a massive block. A stretch of it, as long as a mountain on its side, lay stranded in the shallow water. It was grey and pallid as if it had stopped breathing hours before. I had thought of the reef as a certainty; something made to stay and exist even if people didn't.

As the sun shifted behind a runaway cloud, I thought I saw something moving in the bushes.

'Colonel, I think your goat is over there,' I said, pointing at the twigs.

'Goat's safe,' he said, slapping a rock into a heap of wreckage.

I looked out to the grumbling sea and down at my feet where two tiny shells manoeuvred around my shoe. The sand-crabs were returning. I wasn't sure where they had gone or how they had protected themselves. But I knew that when a storm came the sand-crabs burrowed deep, hid, and then came out to start all over again. Phenomenal waves could dig into the foundation of a house, plough under a reef, but they couldn't carry away the sand-crabs. I moved my feet carefully and walked towards the bushes, to look for the dog, to see if he had survived.

Peter Bennett
STOVIES

It's early evenin when we get back fae the club. Ah've a pot ay stovies left oer fae yesterday in the fridge ah'll heat up fur us. Just the waiy Jeanie used tae make them wae the good butcher's steak links fae the shoap oan Shettleston Road.

Ah'll huv tae get the bloody door open first, mind. Three sheets tae the bloody wind, we ur. Still though, it's allowed noo an again. Oan a day like the day especially.

It wis a good result aw the same. It's nice tae see them win, ye know, the Cellic.

We'd staiyed fur another couple when it finished, but no long efter, ah decided enough wis enough an came up the road, bringin Tam wae me, wae the promise ay gien him a scran.

Some scratchin roon the Yale loack an the key goes in. We stumble in the door an up the loabby. There's a cry ay expletives fae ahent me as Tam stoats his knee aff the wee telephone table ootside the bedroom. Ah turn the loabby light oan tae see him hoppin aboot haudin his shin, ragin.

'Fuckin thing. First ah get a belt in the mooth an noo this. Anythin else ye want tae throw at me the day?' he sais, lookin up tae the ceilin.

'Nae good talkin tae him up there. Ah've been tryin fur seventy-odd year. He either disnae listen, listens an disnae dae anythin tae help, or isnae there tae hear ye in the first bloody place.'

He looks at me in recognition ay the drunken profundity an nods his heid.

It's then ah see it, lyin oan the flair, smashed an in pieces; the picture ah keep there ay Jeanie an I, wae John, Stephanie an young Daniel, when he wis just a baby.

'Ya bloody clown, ye! That's you aw oer the back, that is. Stumblin through life fae wan bloody disaster tae the next. Look at it!' ah sais, pickin up the shattered frame an pullin the photie oot.

It's damaged, the gless huvin scraped the surface, scorin a mark
through mine an John's faces.

Ah turn it oer an see oan the back, in Jeanie's haunwritin:

Daniel's first birthday, August, 1979.

'Ah'm sorry Coyle. Ah never meant tae—'

'Aye? That's it though Tam, ye never *mean* tae but ye still always
dae. Ye never *meant* tae take a swing fur that boay in The Auld
Shipbank that time back when oor time wis just oot, when ah'd
tae wade in an get ye oot ay it when his mates goat involved. Ye
never *meant* it when ye set fire tae the paint store at work an ah
hud tae cover fur ye, doactorin the paperwork an chaingin joab
numbers tae show that ye wurnae workin in that area. An ye never
bloody *meant* tae get yersel up tae yer neck in it wae this swine,
the bastarn money lender. Ye dae know they're just aboot tae start
breakin limbs unless ye come up wae their cash, daint ye?'

'Aye ah fuckin know! They'll just huv tae dae whit they huv tae
dae, well. Ye cannae get blood oot ay a stane. Ah know that much.
Ah'm fucked, int ah? Mind oot the waiy an ah'll clear this up fur
ye,' he sais, bendin doon an pickin up pieces ay gless.

'Never bloody mind it Tam! Ah'll get it. Just away in an sit doon,
wull ye?'

He skulks away, face trippin him, feelin sorry fur himsel an ah
fold the photie in hauf, puttin it in ma inside poakit afore pickin
up the bigger pieces ay gless. Ah sweep the rest up wae a dustpan
an brush an pap it aw in the bin, ben the kitchen.

'Did ye mean that, whit ye sais?' Tam sais, fae the livin room.

'Sorry aboot aw that Tam, it's no your fault bother seems tae
foallie ye aboot.'

'Naw, no that – when ye were sayin aboot God an how he disnae
listen, an it's probably because he's no there. Did ye mean it?'

Ah consider whit ah'm gonae say because at the end ay the day,
who knows eh? Ah mean really. The Bible? Scripture? That's just

ancient propaganda. Apparent proof that the Abrahamic God exists an wants ye tae be fearful ay him; tae bend tae his will – dae so or feel his wrath. That's whit it sais, int it? Load ay bloody pish!

Ye spend yer life fightin tae drag yersel up oot ay the gutter; tae provide fur an raise a faimily, through hardship an destitution, an ye've tae take solace in it bein God's will. Yer misery is whit he wants. Shite ah'm tellin ye! The Church is just another instrument ay oppression utilised tae subjugate us aw!

'Well did ye?' he sais, again.

'Naw Tam, naw. Ah never meant it.'

The 'opium ay the people', that's whit Marx cried it, religion, an ah reckon he wisnae far wrang. If it gies folk comfort – somethin tae haud oan tae – if it anaesthetises them fae the rest ay it, let them huv it. At least that waiy it's aw fur somethin, ah suppose.

Ah open the fridge, grabbin the pot ay stovies an peel the cling-film aff it, settin it doon oan the cooker. Turnin the gas oan low, ah tell Tam tae keep an eye oan it an leave him oan the couch rollin his baccy.

In the wardrobe in the bedroom ah reach up tae the high shelf where ah keep the shoeboax, liftin it doon.

'Ah'm puttin the kettle oan Coyle! Ye wantin a cup ay tea made?' Tam shouts through fae the kitchen.

'Aye. Ah'll no be a minute,' ah sais, openin the boax an liftin the two books (*Dubliners* – James Joyce an *The Ragged-Trousered Philanthropists* – Robert Tressell) aff tae the side, revealin the money underneath.

Ma savins. There's aboot fifteen hunner poun there. Ah wis gonae gie it tae young Daniel when he turns twinty-wan. Mibbe help him get a start wae things. Put a deposit doon oan a hoose mibbe – a wee flat or somethin.

Ah count oot a thoosand poun an leave the rest, levellin it roughly oot in the boax an placin the books back oan tap. Stowin it away back oan the shelf it came fae, ah stick the thoosand ah'd set aside in a broon envelope fae an auld gas bill ah find in the dresser drawer.

Ah'll still see Daniel awright, ah'll make sure ay it. It'll just no be as much as ah'd planned, that's aw.

Ah should've done this afore noo, in truth.

'Here ye are,' ah sais, crumplin the envelope intae his haun, claspin it shut.

'Whit's this?'

'It's fur you. That should be enough tae settle it wae Mullin. They're no gonnae let this go, Tam.'

He opens it, thumbin through the notes. 'Jesus Christ, Coyle. How much is there?'

'There's a grand there. Just take it wae ye an go an see the bastart an put it behind ye.'

'Ah cannae take this. It's too much, ah cannae—'

'Ye'll take it awright! Whit else ur ye gonnae dae, eh? The best ye kin hope fur is they'll kick yer cunt in an take everythin ye've goat tae gie them – this time. They'll be back but. Every fuckin week until ye croak it, which might be sooner than ye think, by the way. How ye gonnae feed yersel, eh? Just bloody take it Tam!'

'Naw ah'll no! Ye sais it yersel! Ah've spent ma life, a nuttin, a fuckin waster! Yer right! An it's aw ma dain, Coyle. At least Jackie came back tae me as an adult. She hud every right tae disown me, like her mother.'

'Mind ay that, eh? How she up an left wae Jackie when she wis just a tote cos ay aw the bevvyin an gamblin? An whit did ah dae, eh? Fuck all, that's whit! Ah just let them; let them go waeoot as much ay a whimper. Couldnae even fight fur them; couldnae even be fuckin fucked dain that. Ah don't deserve Jackie an the grandweans, an they deserve better than a fuckin alkie deadbeat like me in their lives.'

Ah clasp his haun again tightly roon the envelope, feelin his bony knuckles against ma palm. He looks at me, his face ruddied wae a lifetime ay swallyin an eyes glazed wae the pain ay regret.

Ah want tae offer him some words ay reassurance; tae placate him in some waiy; tae gie him convalescence fae himsel, but ah cannae. Every man is a prisoner ay their ain actions, or inaction – a slave tae the memories that haunt them. Ah kin nae mare absolve him ay guilt, than he kin me – fur oor John. Fur Jeanie. Fur mibbe dain things differently, if we hud oor time again.

Whit's fur ye'll no go by ye, that's whit they say. Mare shite! It's maxims like that they bloody want ye tae believe; that ye ur, where ye ur; at yer natural station in life. Ye get whit ye get an ye should be thankful. There's aye folk worse aff than yersel, ye see – always some poor bastart further doon that sheer cliff face we're aw haudin oan tae.

Some ascend the cunt wae ease, happily elbowin others oot their waiy, staunin oan heids an kickin oot at every bastart on their waiy up. Others start oot in loftier positions, fawin further doon wae each wrang step they take. Maist ay us, though, just coorie in, hingin oan tae whitever wee foothold in amongst it aw we kin find.

Aye, it's yer actions right enough, that's whit defines ye. Dain whit needs tae be done. Dain whit ye think's right an hopin that yer moral compass disnae let ye doon.

Inevitably though, at some point, it will, an when that happens, ye've goat tae live wae it. That's aw ye kin dae.

Well, it's no *aw* ye kin dae. Oor John chose another waiy.

Young Daniel thinks he wis a coward, an he's right. He *wis* a bloody coward! He might huv escaped fae whitever it wis that tormented him; fae whitever troubles it wis he deemed insurmountable, but aw he left behind him wis a void. A void that ma Jeanie could never fill again.

The doactors sais it wis her hert an they wur right, just no the waiy they meant it. Her hert wis broke the day John killed himsel. Five year later, the last wee flicker ay a flame that remained went oot.

Whit wis ah sayin again? Aye, ye dae whit's right. An no just fur yersel, fur others tae. That's how ah need tae help Tam. He might no be the finest example ay a man tae ever live an breathe, an he's made mistakes, but he's still here; still fightin his coarner. That counts fur somethin, ye see.

Furbye aw that, he's ma pal.

Ah put doon the cutlery an plates ay stovies oan the wee coffee table in the livin room. Pipin hoat steam rises fae the dish ay stewed sausages, carrots, totties an onion.

There's a wee nip in the air so ah wheel oer the Calor gas fire fae the coarner an click the igniter, turnin it up tae three bars.

Tam's awready wirin intae his plate, scoopin up fork faes like a man bailin watter oot a sinkin boat. 'This is rare, Coyle, ah'll gie ye that. Wis that a plain loaf in there ah seen? A couple ay slices ay that wae butter wid be magic,' he sais.

*

It's dark when ah wake up. Ah've goat the wee tartan throw that normally hings oer the back ay the couch draped oer me, an Tam's seat's empty, the plates an glesses cleared away.

We'd hud a nightcap – a dram ay Johnnie Walker – an ah must've dozed aff.

Liftin the square boatle aff the table an haudin it up tae slivers ay orange streetlight comin in through the blinds, ah see there's aboot an inch left in the bottom ay it. It wis hauf bloody full when ah goat it oot the scullery.

Ah go ben the kitchen tae get a drink ay watter. The dishes an tumblers are washed an dried, sittin oan the rack.

Lettin it overflow, leavin the tap runnin fur a wee minute till the watter's cauld enough, ah fill a gless, take a drink an head fur ma bed.

In the loabby, oan the wee table, the envelope, wae the money still inside, sits next tae the phone.

Karen Elizabeth Bishop
CAIRN

strainslake, we try. where meadows of light like grief expanding,
our hands two animal hearts we wax undone toward the upslope,
knees first then mouths. the bees again and the antlers, the hum.

we conquer nothing, contrive of cairns with our feet and stones,
the kidney slacks and the pancreas. we invented saints for you &
fools. kid rhymes laced with wishes and condemnation. horses

and ladies' horses and gullets, cabbages and pockets, bells and
wicks, storysticks. in what corner of the forest, we hiss, does the
wasp gather to consider our future: shrill, merciless, untired. we

wait for the sharp songsting, a warning to recede, the communal
thrum of waist and wing, the voices thrown together like clouds
coming. but first a stone upon the flat stone, cross-stones piled

like winter tears, but was it a bird bent against the wind or if we
read it twice will we remember: here we've been, here a measure
of our trust, an early grave but also in time we speak in tongues

that fathom distance and ways out, we partition a dark sight from a
bright, we lean, we lend, we mend ourselves to a bend at the break,
raise our hands to shield a sunlit eye, pockets full of rocks, we rise.

Nathan Breakenridge
UPSTAIRS

The rain had started sometime in the afternoon. Michael sat in his car and stared across the road at the tenement door, waiting for the rain to stop. It didn't, so he pulled his jacket tight around him and set off jogging.

The wind harried him as he went, shouted after him as he shut the door at his back. He stood in the dim light of the close with his eyes shut. He could smell the dead leaves clumped around the walls and at the bottom of the first step. He tried to remember a dream he had had the night before, found he couldn't, and started up the stairs.

The building was an old one. The stone steps hammocked in the middle from decades of footfall. He had been living there for months but never passed anyone on the stairs. He had joked once that it was like coming through an airlock.

When he reached the landing outside their door, he heard a loud noise come from the floor above, the top floor. Like someone had dropped something heavy. He stood and listened for a little while, then shook his head and took out his keys.

Meghan was standing in the living room with her head out of the open window. He could hear her breathing from the hall. When he put his hands on her hips she said, It's like a cold drink of water, I love it. She took another deep breath and turned around, pushing Michael's hands back to his own sides and holding them there. How was it? she said.

The same.

Still nothing?

I might as well not be there.

She squeezed his hands and let them go, then turned back to the window and shut it. Petrichor, she said, That's what it's called. I looked it up.

No, I told you that.

Well, I forgot then looked it up.

She poked his arm on the way past him to the breakfast bar that separated the living room from the kitchen. She lifted a cup that was there and sipped from it and put it down again.

Cold? Michael said.

I don't know how I manage it. Swear I just made it. She lifted the cup again and carried it over to the sink. I haven't done anything about dinner either.

We can get a takeaway. Calendar says it's Friday. He gestured to the word-a-day calendar on the fridge, dated over a week ago. The word of the day had been *lambent*.

Aye, let's do that, she said, not looking up from the cup. I keep going to do things then I end up just staring into space.

The weather won't be helping, he said.

Meghan rinsed the cup in the sink and set it on the draining board. She stood in the kitchen squeezing her sides for a while. Sally's wanting me to meet her at the Algae. First time for about a year. I feel like a charity case.

Well, something different's good. There's football on anyway. He had pulled his phone from a pocket and was reading something on the screen. Have you heard anything from the guy upstairs? he said.

Is it a guy? I've never seen him.

Did you hear him drop something there?

I thought that was you. But aye, he's been moving about a lot. It sounds like he's maybe running? It must be a different layout; I don't know how he's got space for it.

Michael was still wearing his jacket. He went back into the hall and hung it on a hook. When he came back into the living room he said, I don't know that it's a guy, I just assumed. Maybe he's doing the place up.

There was another thud from the ceiling, and a brief, thin cry. That sounded like a guy, said Michael.

Do you think he's all right?

They both stood still and quiet for a moment. There was a sound of footsteps from above. Aye, he's fine.

*

Sally was sitting at a table by the bar when Meghan got there. She had a bottle of rosé waiting.

The pub was quiet, but not empty. There were songs playing on the jukebox by the door that Meghan recognised from when she was a teenager. She smiled and sipped her wine while Sally talked, and watched the people at the other tables and the man behind the bar. He had a stud in the middle of his bottom lip and wore a bandana.

It happened to my maw as well, before she had me, Sally was saying, And what the doctor said was that she should just try and get pregnant again, straight away, that was the only thing for it. Soon as possible. She drank some of her wine. How's Mikey doing? Actually, hang on, I need a pee. She stood up and walked off towards the back of the pub.

Meghan looked into her glass for a while and then up at the bar. There was an older man being served. He asked the barman in the bandana for water. Just to take a pill, son, he said. The barman started to fill a glass from a tap before the man waved at him to stop. A bottle if you please, son.

I'd need to charge you.

That's fine. That's no bother at all.

The barman handed him a glass bottle with a blue cap out of the fridge. When he brought him his change the older man said, Do you know what it is they put in the tap water, son? To clean it, that is?

Can't say I do, said the barman, already moving to serve someone at the other end of the bar.

Rat poison, the man said, nodding, Rat poison.

*

Michael came out of the toilet and went straight to the kitchen and pulled another can from the fridge. He opened it and took a sip, then looked over the breakfast bar at the TV. It was halftime so he'd muted it. He watched the three men in suits nodding and gesturing.

Another bang from the flat upstairs made him jump. He squeezed the can and a little liquid frothed out and over his fingers and dribbled onto the linoleum. He looked up at the ceiling but it was quiet again. He used his socked foot to mop up the spill then went back around the breakfast bar and sat down on the couch.

He leaned over and lifted one of the empty cans that were lying by his feet and set it on top of one that was standing upright. He stacked the other two in the same way. He sat back.

He sipped his full can and wondered why none of the three men on the screen were wearing ties with their suits. He knew who two of them were but not the third. The third man was perfectly bald but had a short, dark beard, neatly clipped. Michael tried to decide if he looked familiar. He didn't think so, and neither did the other men, he decided. Three suits and no ties and no faces.

There was another thump from the ceiling. Two things had been dropped in quick succession. Michael stared at the spot where he thought the sound had come from, in the corner above the TV.

There was another sound like something softer slapping against the upstairs floor. Michael sat very still and listened to something drag itself around on the other side of the ceiling.

*

Meghan got the bus back around eleven. She stopped inside the front door of the building to message Sally but got no reply. When she got to their landing, she heard a door open upstairs.

Meghan said nothing and pulled her keys out of her bag, then said, Hello? She waited for a moment, then heard the door close and a lock slide back into place.

She had expected Michael to still be awake when she got in but all the lights were out. She found her way to her side of the bed by the light of her phone pointed at the floor. She could just make out Michael, curled up tightly under the duvet.

In a dream that night she banged at the ceiling with an old-fashioned broom handle, until she felt something jerk it up through the plaster, and she was pulled, squealing, into the darkness above.

*

Michael's phone started buzzing around seven. It was still dark. He screwed up his face and reached over to grab it. It took him three tries to swipe the alarm off, then he dropped the thing onto his chest and let his arms go limp. He could hear Meghan still snoring lightly.

He managed to sit up and put his head in his hands. He looked at Meghan. She was lying on her front with her arms underneath her pillow. Her breathing had become shallower and difficult to hear. He wondered if she would look any different if she were dead.

His headache got worse when he stood up. In the bathroom he stared at his reflection in the mirror above the sink. He had lost weight.

He went back into the bedroom and pulled on a hoody and his green shorts and went through to the kitchen. He bent down and opened the cupboard under the sink and reached in until his hand found the skinny handle of a plastic bag. He checked behind him and listened for a while, then pulled the bag full of cans carefully out from behind the washing machine and took it into the hall. He slipped on his trainers and put his hood up, then unlocked the door and went out.

The morning was cold. The streetlamps were still on but a lighter grey was creeping up over the rooftops. He went round the corner to the recycling bins, opened one and swung the bag in. Then he went back inside.

*

Meghan woke up a little later to the sound of the front door closing. She lay there for over an hour, struggling to focus on her phone. When she got up she poached an egg but left it sitting in the water to go cold after the smell made her gag. The shower ran especially hot and she spent a long time perched naked on the edge of the bath with her head under the stream. When she turned it off she realised the water had been running down her back and had soaked the floor.

She managed to mop up the water and do the dishes but left the hoover sitting in front of the cupboard she had pulled it from. She stood in front of the living room window and tried to decide whether the rain was too heavy to go out in, straining to make out the sizes of the ripples on puddles. There was a loud creak and more footsteps from upstairs. She watched the ceiling for a while, tracking the sounds. When they seemed to move across the room and out into the hall, she followed.

She followed the sounds towards the bathroom, walking at pace now with whoever was upstairs. They stopped over the bath. Meghan climbed in and looked up at the ceiling. She felt her socks turning wet. The mop was still leaning against the wall. She leaned over and lifted it, then stepped up onto the side of the bath and stretched as far as she could but could only graze the ceiling. She gripped the damp head of the mop with both hands and lunged upwards, managing to just tap the plaster before she lost her balance and stepped heavily back down onto the floor. She stared up at the ceiling, panting a little. There was a mark where the handle of the mop had scuffed the paint. She noticed a noise then, and turned her head to listen better. A tapping, light and hollow, just on the other side of the mark. She thought it sounded like Morse code from an old film. An index finger tapping out a message through her ceiling. She put on a waterproof and went out.

The rain rang like static on her hood. She walked down to the river and stopped to watch some ducks sheltering under the trees on the bank. Two of them were asleep and the other looked like it was trying to wake them. The sight of the ducks made her well up. She spent most of the afternoon walking along the riverside, crying.

*

Michael came back late and red-eyed. He found Meghan sitting on the couch with the TV turned down low. A newsreader was looking grave in front of an image of a crying child in a desert.

That guy's at it, he said when he came in.

Who?

Your man, he said, pointing at the ceiling, He was out on the landing watching for somebody.

You saw him?

Nah, I could hear him, he was panting. Must be a junkie.

I hope he's all right.

*

The running kept up intermittently for the rest of the night. After a while it was as if Meghan couldn't hear it anymore, but Michael found himself tensing at every sound, gritting his teeth in anticipation in between.

When they went to bed, he lay awake on his back, tracking the sound of feet scuttling in circles around the flat above, from the living room, over the kitchen into the bedroom, then through the wall to the bathroom, then up the hall and back into the living room. He found himself following the sounds with his eyes.

He looked over at Meghan. He wanted to wake her up but decided against it. The footsteps had slowed down, were moving now at what Meghan would call museum pace. They made their way down the hall and into the living room, to the far wall and back again. Over the kitchen. Into the bedroom. He heard them stop directly above where he was lying. There was a heavy clatter of knees against a floor, a slap of palms on wood. There was quiet after that.

It took him a long time to fall asleep. He woke to early daylight and the sound of tapping coming through the ceiling. He sat up and swung himself off of the mattress. He heard Meghan groan when the legs of his jeans slapped against the floor.

The door to the flat upstairs was the dark green of pine needles. He noticed there was a nail sticking out of the wood, just below the spyhole. He wondered whether it was for hanging wreaths at Christmas. He knocked heavily on the door.

The sound echoed in the empty close. He could just make out a kind of shuffling from inside the flat. He knocked again, pounding with the soft underside of his fist.

The shuffling stopped. He stepped back from the door. Nothing else happened. He went to knock a third time but instead crouched down to see if he could spot any movement through the keyhole.

Squatting there in the dim close, Michael thought suddenly of a house where he had lived as a boy, maybe nine or ten. Between the main road and the fence at the bottom of the garden there had been a copse of birches. He would push his way through a gap in the fence behind the shed and wander around among the pale trees. He remembered how he used to think the knots and whorls in their waxy flesh looked like eyes. He had found one that was deeper than the others, that must have been hollowed out for a nest. He had crouched there, just as he was now, staring into that hole in the birch tree. He had seen something move.

Michael stood up straight, frowning at the memory. He couldn't remember what had happened next. He turned around and started back down the stairs. He must have run, he thought. Surely he must have run home.

Niki Brennan
GATHER

My father has a new gun now, it's shining from a hook on the cabin wall. It's the first thing I notice when I enter the room. The second is the deer that lies on the table between us, opened up like a birthday present. I sit down on the couch and watch. He has his hands inside the carcass, all the way to the elbows, unwrapping it from the inside out. There's a plastic sheet underneath to collect the blood and pieces of organ.

So, how are you? he says to the deer.

Fine, I say to the deer.

He nods. He pulls out its liver. When he drops it onto the plastic he gives it a slap for good measure. He nods. His beard is more salt than pepper now, his belly hangs over his jeans and his front four teeth are yellowing. There's still something handsome left in him though, tucked away in his laughter lines and his strong jawline and his warm eyes that look not unlike the deer's.

Have you been up to much?

Just work and uni.

Are you still working at— He stops. The crease between his eyebrows deepens. He rummages around.

The deli?

Aye. I was about to say it.

Nah, not for a year. I'm working in a bar now.

Right.

Just until I finish uni.

Right.

The intestines come out like those long ropes of sausages in kids' cartoons.

How's that going? he asks after dropping the intestines on top of the liver.

Uni?

Aye.

Fine. I just got a first in my psychology essay.

He nods. I watch him skin the deer, then fillet it.

*

We impale some of the venison on a spit and build up a fire underneath it. I'm in charge of revolving it every so often. Its skin sears and bubbles and drips down to sizzle on the coals as the barbecued meat smell is carried around in the smoke. He rolls skinny little cigarettes. It takes him roughly twelve seconds to roll each one. The tips of his fingers are yellow. He sips his beer. I sip my beer. The sky is darkening, the sun and a curve of the moon just about level in the sky. I slap a midge on my arm then scrape it off and flick it into the fire.

*

When I was eight, maybe, I was playing a game out on the grass. I was trying to collect bugs in my hands, careful not to crush them completely, and move them onto one wide flower. I'd hunt them on blades of grass and lying in the bell of daffodils and on the spongey underbelly of moss-covered logs. I'd carry them all to this one flower and try to make them coexist. Mostly the ones I placed there would scatter before I returned with more, but sometimes the insects would stare at each other, all scared to break the standoff. Sometimes they would fight. It was interesting to watch them tear each other up.

*

I was playing this game when two pheasants wandered out of the treeline. I didn't know what they fuck they were. Big parrots probably. I started to crawl through the grass towards them, their feathers brilliant in the sunlight. I didn't know what I'd do if I got close, I just wanted to be near them. The birds heard something and cocked their heads. Then there was a bang, and one of the birds exploded in a mist of blood and feathers. The other bird bounded back into the trees, I cowered in the grass. My father's footsteps thumped past me as he gave chase. I got to my knees and looked down at my palm, where the bug I'd been holding was smeared in red and black. My father walked back from the woods as I was standing over the bird's body. He said some cliché shit about everything needing to eat or the circle of life or something like that. I just stared at what was left of the bird and listened to its girlfriend cooing from the trees.

*

We eat the venison with our hands, too hungry to care about the grease burning our fingers and our chins. We eat in silence, only stopping to drain our beers. I go and get two more from the fridge. It contains eighteen beers, a tub of mustard, some meat wrapped up in plastic and one lonely pickle drifting around in the sediment at the bottom of its jar. I open up the drawer next to it to find the bottle opener; it's empty but for a bullet that rolls toward me. I hold it in my palm, it's cold and heavy. A finger from a hand reaching out of its deathbed.

*

Couldn't find the opener, I say when I get back outside.

Cause it's out here.

Aw, shit so it is.

He hands me it and I open both and pass him one. We finish off the venison and lick our fingers and watch the midges flying in circles above us.

Can I roll a cigarette?

Since when did you smoke?

Uni. Bad habit.

He grunts and passes me the pouch.

I pinch the skin, tuck a filter in the end, stub a wad of tobacco in, tuck, lick and roll.

Seventeen seconds.

I wonder if I imagine the smile on his face when he passes
me the lighter. He rolls one too. We smoke and listen to the
fire crackling. I want to say some shit about how it's nice being
away from all the light pollution so there's more stars. But I just
stay quiet.

You must miss seeing stars like that, he says.

Yeah, I guess so, I say. He nods and gazes up at them.

*

We drink a couple more beers, neither of us saying much. He
never lets the fire go out; it's always stretching up to be a metre tall.
My cheeks are red, my jumper smells like smoke. I realise I could
live out here. Be something else. Try it on. How easy it would
be, like giving in.

So, how's—

Nattingya? he answers.

I was going to say that, I say. I wasn't.

Sure. I don't know. Haven't spoke to her in a while.

You not been over to see her?

Nah I finished that.

How come?

Aw you know. Just wasn't feeling it. He belches and it echoes
around the woods. Flights were a fortune anyway.

Aye.

You eh— you seeing— anybody? He doesn't look at me when
he asks it. He fumbles for a cigarette.

Nah. Broke up with my girlfriend a few months ago.

He seems to relax a bit at that. Oh right, you're still young, he
says while blowing out smoke.

Aye. You too.

He nods and smiles. He sips his beer. The smile drops off his
face into the dark when he looks away.

*

In the morning the birds are singing a strange song, like the noise of walking down a foreign street. There is cold sunlight in the spare room where I'm staying, and dust caught up and floating in it. I can smell the smoke and the barbecue. The house is quiet. I stare at the photo pinned to the wall opposite my bed like a wanted poster. It's only half of a photo, and my mother is on the half that's left. She has a monkey on her shoulder and a jungle stretches out behind her, she's tanned and smiling. Her face is beautiful in the photo, all sharp lines and freckles. I turn on my side and read over old text messages.

*

He is drinking a beer and eating some venison with eggs when I get up.
    You want one?
    I hesitate. Yeah, why not.
    He hands me a beer.
    Where did the eggs come from?
    The chickens. They're fresh.
    Aw, nice.
    You want to go fishing today?
    Aye, okay.
    There are more eggs in the kitchen.

*

It's not really a beach, just the loch and a brown strip of small stones that leads to a darker strip of bigger stones framed by nettles and thistles. He already has the line through the holes on his rod and is fixing bait to the hook at the end. It's a small worm, wriggling and covered in dirt. He pinches it and threads the hook through one of its ends, wrapping it through its body. It bobs around in the air with the lead weight. I'm struggling with poking the line through the smallest hole at the end. The sun is high in the clear sky but the breeze cuts across the water and turns my hands red and stiff. My tongue pokes out my mouth as I squint.

I always had to get your mother to do that. She had smaller hands than me. Better eyes too.

I don't say anything. I don't turn around; I tense up like I've been caught sneaking around someone else's house. He coughs and starts rummaging in his bag for something. The water is perfectly still.

*

I clamber onto the little boat as he holds it steady, facing me, the rods on the floor in a puddle of water. He begins rowing us out into the middle of the loch. I watch a great grey heron perched on a rock that juts out of the water like a broken bone. It unsheathes its long neck and leans out across the water, the ripples of our movement reaching his rock and tricking him into thinking there's a fish underneath the surface. We glide along the grey pane of the water, neither of us looking at the other.

Do you still remember how? he asks when we stop.

Aye, hold the line here and whip it in then let go until it sinks a bit and then watch the float.

Basically. If you hook something pull like this and reel at the same time.

Okay. I hold the line in the first crease of my index finger, draw the rod past a right angle from my body then whip it towards the water, letting go of the line and watching with satisfaction as it sails across the water then lands to sink a good distance from the boat.

Nice.

Cheers. I rest the rod against the side of the boat and open a beer, palming it down off the rim. He lets his line fly; it goes much further than mine. He opens a beer in the same way. I notice there's a family of deer grazing at the grass on the opposite side of the loch.

Deer. I point.

Aye.

Feel kinda guilty.

Why?

Cause we're eating one for lunch.

Don't. Everything has to eat. We're just lucky to be at the top of the food chain.

I try not to laugh. Do you remember telling me that before?

He hesitates, glancing at me then adjusts something on his rod.

I do.

I nod.

We sip our beers. We watch our orange floats bobbing around in the water. It's surprising how easy it is to slip into nothing out here, staring into the gentle water, not thinking or doing anything, just existing until something happens to you that breaks up the emptiness.

Eventually my rod starts twitching and I see the float jumping in the water. I pull the rod up and start reeling frantically.

You've got something.

I grunt.

Watch your line.

I whip the rod up and it arches with the strain, curving in the air towards the water. I try to reel.

Watch your line.

I can feel the fish edging closer to the boat, like it's getting sucked into a drain every time I yank and pull and spin the reel. It's giving up. It's near the boat. My muscles are straining, I'm trying to stay steady on my feet as the boat rocks underneath me. I nearly have it.

Then, the rod snaps back and shudders.

Then, the sudden release of tension.

Then, I told you to watch your line.

I thought I fucking had it.

He pauses. Well you didn't.

I can see that.

I start dissecting what's left of the line and threading through a new one.

Don't worry about it, there's plenty more fish in the loch.

I know that.

Good.

Good.

I pull and stretch my bad mood until it lightly covers everything.

If you don't want to fish we could go back and get the gun, take it into the woods?

Do you really think I want to take the fucking gun out?

He looks at me like he's stumbled into a mother bear protecting a cub.

No, I guess not.

We go quiet.

You've got something, I say a few minutes later, noticing his rod is twitching.

Aw, fuck. He takes it up and controls its jerking, breathing through his nose, he reels it slowly, stops, lifts it a little, reels, stops. That's it. The rod is bending and straining but he barely moves. After about a minute he begins reeling faster, pulling up on the rod, but still remaining perfectly calm.

Catch it, he says, a few seconds before a fish breaks the water and slams up the side of the boat to flail around on the floor. I catch it in the net and it begins to calm down.

Little mackerel.

Aye?

Aye. He looks up at me, his hand clinching the fish against the floor. He grins, then laughs and claps me on the shoulder like it was me who caught it. I'm surprised to realise that I wish it was. He reaches for a small metal bat and strikes the fish three times on the head. It stops moving. He sets it aside, then sets up his rod and sends the line out again. The water feels like it's flowing a little faster, the trees and the grass bending slightly in the wind.

*

When we head back we have five fish, apparently four mackerel and one rainbow trout. I carry them in the net into the house, I can see their eyes bulging through the gaps, occasionally they slap off my leg and leave a slimy trail. Inside, I empty them out into the sink and wash them down.

You want me to do it? he asks.

Nah I've got it.

I don't remember teaching you how—

You didn't.

Aw. Right.

I find a small filleting knife, pick a mackerel and start cutting off its fins, before scraping off some of its smooth scales. I pierce its belly by the tail-end and run the knife along towards the head.

Fuck. Ew.

Worms. They pour out of the fish like bile, still wriggling. I drop it with a shiver and wash my hands.

What's up?

Full of worms.

Aw, shite. He comes over and takes the knife, opening up the rest. All but the trout are filled with the parasite.

Looks like someone's having deer again, he says.

Great.

He nods, focuses on washing his hands.

You hear the one about the deer with no eyes?

I look at him, just in time to see the dumb smile slide off his face and drip onto the floor by the soap and the water and the worm that escaped the sink.

I shake my head and walk into my room. I sit on the edge of the bed and fold, the final pages of a book slammed shut. I give

myself that. That moment to do nothing but break. Then I get
up and I cross the room and I rip off that photo and finish the
job, tearing it into more pieces until my mother is a jigsaw that I
can't put back together and she falls through my fingers onto
the floor, where I land.

*

That's where he finds me, I guess about an hour later. I'm all dried
up and crusty. The only light in the room is the moon landing
softly on the bed. He knocks first.

You okay? he asks, barely in the room.

I'm fine.

You sure?

It's just hard being here.

Look— we should talk about it.

Should we?

Well we haven't, not since—

I know.

We should talk about it, he says, more certain this time.

Fine. I get up and walk past him, through the cabin and out
into the night. I sit down and open a beer. He joins me.

We chew the silence up, working over it until it's fat and mis-
shapen between us.

I wish it had been me. That found her. Not you, he says, finally.

So do I.

He nods.

You know the worst part? I didn't even know it was her, I
say, finally.

What—

She was wearing that jumper you bought her for her fortieth.
That's how I knew.

The blue one. I remember that.

Yeah.

He shudders next to me, looking off in the other direction. He keeps shuddering. I realise he's crying. My hand hovers over his back, stuck in the air, not knowing whether to swoop or to find somewhere else to land. It drops, his back is warm, it heaves against the rocks.

Mikey Burnett
IT'S LADLE

Ah hink, what ah'll miss maire, than anyhing else, is her laugh. It saddens, if no destroys me, that ah'll probably never hear it again. It wis a soartae crackle. An endearin, intoxicatin crackle. That's honestly the best wey ah kin describe it. And sometimes. Well, quite oaftin, in fact. She yased tae laugh sae hard that it actually soonded quite saire. And the maire she became overcome wae hysteria, the maire you wanted tae laugh tae. It wis class, likes. And, aye. It wis pretty contagious. Ah mind this yin night, eh? Long before she foond oot aboot me and the domme. A time when you'd huv hud yur mortgage oan the pair ae us yin day settlin doon tae a marriage and hayin bairns. A period ae ma life, and ah suppose, her's tae. When happiness wis as routine as wakin up tae daylight and the soonds ae singin birds. Oan this particular night we wur baith sat thegither huddin hands oan the couch in her mum and dad's livin room. The telly wis oan and this quiz show wis jist aboot tae start. Cannae mind the name ae it now, likes. But as soon as the intro music began playin, suddenly the three ae them goat aw excited. It wis clearly suttin they enjoyed watchin as a family. And even though, tae be honest, ah wished fur the telly tae explode, or an unexpected power cut tae happen. Ah decided tae jist sit there like a gid boay and keep ma critical opinions tae masel. But before the annoyin presenter hud even concluded his embarrassinly unfunny openin comedy bit, Brooke's dad smugly suggests fur us tae pair up against each other as couples. Him and his wife, gone heid tae heid, wae me, and his daughter. Brooke immediately accepts his challenge. She yased tae play fives at Leith links, likes. Ah yased tae go doon there tae watch her fur support. She hated tae lose. Ah kent how competitive she wis, and obviously, so did he. She'd be desperate tae win. Me and him baith kent it. Only there wis a hurdle fur her tae jump first if she wanted this desire tae become a reality. Which wis bein burdened by the handicap that wis ma limited intellect. That cunt never did like me, yae see. He kent we hud nae fuckin chance ae winnin. Ah mean, ah'm no sayin ah'm thick, or anyhin. But ah did spend the hale ae high school in foondy English fur a reason. So, needless tae say, general knowledge isnae exactly ma hing. And so, ah wis certain ae what the dad wis up tae. He wis intent oan nuttin else except fae embarrassin me. Thus, demonstratin tae his beautiful daughter what a complete retard she wis shaggin. Anywey, the questions soon start comin in at an alarmin rate. And ma heid wis quickly spinnin at aw the answers ah didnae ken. Brooke wis dain well though. Correctly namin capital cities ae countries ah'd never heard ae. And even political stuff which might as well huv been asked in fuckin Chinese. The dad though, the auld prick. Fuck me, ah kin see his puss now. Oh, god, wis he no lovin it. As him and his wife sat decisively miles aheid in the scorin. Aw his condescendin wee smirks aimed firmly in ma direction, tae. They telt me jist how much he wis revellin in ma uselessness. And ah bet if he huda stood up ah wida cloacked his hardon. Mean, it wis sae obvious the bastard wis only playin against me. The clueless mute sat opposite him. Who's yince adorin girlfriend wis nae longer huddin his hand. By the half-wey stage ah foond massel prayin fur a fitbaw question. He doesnae like fitbaw. Hates it, in fact. The middle-class bore prefers rugby. But alas, it never came. What did come insteed though wis an unexpected opportunity. Ma chance, or so ah thoat, fur a wee bit ae redemption. And maire importantly, the chance tae git it right fuckin up him.

'*Name a five letter word for a large spoon?*' As soon as the presenter finished askin the question ah wis instantly up oot ma seat. And no jist a slow rise, either. It wis a literal leap. 'TABLE!' ah screamed. At the toap ae ma lungs 'FUCKIN TABLE!'

Wae this there wis nae 'Well done, Mark' fae Brooke. Which in aw honestly, is what ah hud expected. Insteed, the answer ah gave wis greeted by only silence. And as ah looked at the three ae them aw ah saw wis a trio ae pusses painted in sheer disbelief.

Obviously, ah kent right there and then that ah musta said suttin wrong. Although ah wis genuinely certain that tablespoon wis worth at least a few points. But then it happened. There she went. Brooke burst intae a fit ae uncontrollable laughter. And ah'm tellin yae. It wis as if she'd jist heard the funniest hing that hus ever been said by anycunt in the history ae the entire world. She stands up tae meet me but she's laughin sae hard that she's oan unsteady feet. So, she grabs oantae me. Pits her airms aroond me and say's 'It's ladle!' before proceedin tae piss hersel even harder. As wur huddin each other ah'm still wonderin what's sae funny and tryin tae figure oot exactly what 'It's ladle' means. But then ah catch the dad's morbid puss. And that's when it dawned oan me that 'it's ladle' musta been the correct answer. So, of course, ah start laughin tae. As if ah wis in oan the joke aw along. But, see, it wisnae jist Brooke's crackle that wis geein me the buzz. It wis also the fact that her faithers plans tae oot me as a stupid cunt hud somehow backfired. Cos he wis sat there lookin aw miserable and borderline suicidal cos Brooke still loved me. Even though he proved ah wis thick, right enough. She loved me nae matter what. And there wis nuttin he or anyboady could dae tae change that. Or at least, that's what, in that moment, me and him baith thoat. Little did we ken though that ah could change it aw by massel. Withoot his help. And now there's nuttin ah kin dae, fae here in oot. That wid ever make her crackle again.

Emily Christie
HOMES IN MANY CITIES

I am a lucky woman, I have homes in many cities. It's not as difficult as anyone makes it out to be, you just have to be willing to take what you want.

In Edinburgh I choose old and stately, with solid bones. I know I'll have to gut it completely but it's worth it for the prestige, a chance to breath in the faded, cracked opulence. I wrap myself in its elegance, as though by simply standing in it I may soak up some of that lazy, languid confidence of the gentry. I drink in the harshly lined façade and poke around in the crumbling plaster and see it for its fragility, the façade of excellence with the rotten core. This house tells the truth of the world. After enough time we all rot the same.

For my crumbling Edinburgh home there is no possibility of restoration, I fear the parasite of time and my own over-confident assertions on the property have cast it into ruin. But I can find another. I always find another.

No matter how regal, they crumble in my hands. Some people flip homes, I seem to sink them.

He serves me well, my Edinburgh home, I live off him for a time, but every feast must end and I am bound to the road, to travel and drag my wet trail of destruction across the world.

I leave him – my Edinburgh home – much diminished, I'm afraid. His ribs I cracked and re-slotted to make a roof leak and his skin is shrunken and torn. I guess that's the issue with old and stately, there's too much existing wear and tear. I carry his ear with me, a home away from home, some white hairs still curling from the dark whorl in the centre. I study the swirling vortex spiralling inwards to nothing, my thumb worries at his lobe as I travel, always onward, to find my next home.

In Florence I crave youth, the soft pinks and blues of frescoes and whispery, dreamy pillowy furnishings. I find my home so easily,

I guess it's a buyer's market. I drape myself in the blue and pink of my fantasies, ropes of it, I wind it around my limbs like robes. I burrow into the soft interiors, loll in the softness of my home's interiors. What a shame though, the foundations aren't strong enough. I find myself suffocated, stifling in the heat and dark of his stomach, sickened when the blue turns purple and the pink putrefies. I am expelled from my home earlier than I would have liked, the outside comes in, intruding all too quickly. I share my abode with crawling flies and insects, I try to persevere until I see the colours turn garish and the buzzing becomes unbearable.

I decide city life isn't for me, the noise and colours offend me. I flee to the country, disappointed by how my dreams have deflated but equally ready for the next challenge, the next chance at making a house a home.

Somewhere in the south of France I arrive, feeling swollen in the heat, my fingers fat with pulsing blood as I sweep through the endless winding, dusty roads, my legs coated in mud. Amongst the tall grass and leaning trees I feel as though the reddened tips of my fingers might burst and tiny branches with pink buds will stretch from my broken skin towards the sunlight, that I will be rooted, finally, eternally, my wandering over. Nature consumes me, flies land at the corners of my gasping mouth, thirst makes me rasp and choke, but I refuse to stop.

My wandering always pays off. I decide I need a farmhouse, to marry the nature which assaults me with the cooling comfort of a new home, to wrestle the wild into something malleable which I can control. My new house is nothing much to look at, rustic, a little simple, worn down by the sun and the passing of many seasons, but I find it charming. I come upon it by surprise, in an unassuming field. It was tanned and cracked, like the ground it stood on. It didn't welcome me, dirty as I was, but I got in, fighting my way through the rusty, wheezing gates to claim it as my own.

I stay for a while, shielded from the sun, cocooned in a hammock of muscle-bound limbs which I tore and wove together, inspired by the wicker baskets I pass in markets. I like to think I found solace, peace, but farmhouses require work, upkeep, constant patching and hammering and the weather is oppressive. Before I know it that keening hunger is telling me to move again, to drive forwards.

At the back of my mind, beyond the gnawing starvation which drives me, the ambition which keeps my legs pedalling and eyes scanning like some great automaton, I know I am looking for the one. The home for life, somewhere I can settle. In deciding my next location this sentiment rings in my ears, hollow and crass, helping me make my choice. Who craves that more than Americans?

My journey is arduous, the furthest I've travelled in search of a home, but adventurous women must leave what they know, always plough forward, onwards into the unknown, driven by that essential bone-deep lust for experience, for self-betterment, for fleeting satisfaction.

The swamp heat of Florida coats my lungs and I ride through the flats like a carrion bird, low and circling, mind unravelling with possibilities. I look at flat, squat houses packed in close together, long, thin apartments, gaudy McMansions with sparkling extensions. I've never waited so long for a home but I want to get it right this time, to give fully and bask in a perfect home.

I feel the cold of homelessness, the whistling wind that follows me even indoors, the expanse of the world which threatens to swamp me. I imagine the street I walk on suddenly folding in half, my fragile body being consumed by the sticky concrete, caught between the jaws of the pavement, the cars on the road like molars, grinding me to a pulp. I've never been a lover of the great outdoors. I need a home, fast.

I find my next domicile. It is chosen out of desperation and ease, but I am determined to labour, to give as much as I take. I make a picket fence out of pearly white teeth, a tree house out of a thatch of thinned hair, I construct a porch out of finger bones, boiled clean by the sun. I work harder than I ever have, to make this house a home. I weave and snap and saw and stack until my arms shake from exertion. I look at the fruit of my labour and see only the flaws, the cracked enamel, the gaps in the grouting. I feel sunk in the work, my precious time sucked into the endlessly hungry maw of a house which creaks and shakes and reveals its flaws with uncaring banality.

I howl my anguish into the cold halls, thrash and tear apart my work until my house lies in ruins, tattered. It hurts me to look at it, the wasted potential, the promise and excitement so quickly turned to scraps. My hard work looks like the abandoned creations of a child. I feel chastised by my own ambition. I leave my house quickly, without a plan, feeling unwelcomed, judged by the eyes I'd so stylishly repurposed as bookends, which watched me from the mantelpiece.

Cast out once more I curl in on myself, my arms hugging my ribs as though I can hold my aching, trembling torso together with only my weak grip. I sob, assaulted by the outrage of the outside world. Homeless once more. I am beaten, by the rain, the horns and squawks, the stammered voices which circle me, dizzying, too loud.

I squeeze myself harder and I feel it, the frantic thrum of repetitive beats, my heart, battering me from the inside, reaching out, longingly. I press my hands to the pulsing organ, ecstatic, my fingers play along my chest, dipping into the grooves of my ribs, pressing until I grasp at the cage which so tenderly holds my reliable heart. I grab at my belly, fistfuls of flesh writhing under my eager hands. Here I am, the raw materials for my very own dream house, the one I've always been searching for. I grip my breasts, feel their weight, their warmth, the possibility.

My body feels new, mouldable, like clay, the opportunities of my flesh are tantalising. The world is too bright, too harsh, too brash, I want to crawl into myself where no one can find me, unable to wander, unable to leave. I want to be cocooned, fossilised, make my body my home. I finally know what they mean, home is where the heart is.

I begin construction, or maybe it's demolition, but room must be made. It's more difficult working on myself, my other homes were pliable and as I balance my tools on my knees I wonder if this is a lease I can afford.

But then my other homes dance through my mind, a parade of vacant, rotting disappointments with sagging eaves, damp walls and leaking roofs. I know this is it, that there comes a time for rest, a time to sit back and watch and finally settling sounds lovely, a luxury I never thought I'd be able to afford.

I'll begin with the foundation, just below my belly button, I'll create the home I've dreamed of and I won't leave room for the disappointment which plagues me with every prior endeavour. I feel at peace as I pierce for the first time.

They'll find me curled up, arms wrapped, untouchable, a woman with many houses, finally home.

Kate Coffey
STRATUS CLOUDS DO NOT PRECIPITATE

A long low cloud is drifting over the loch, we gaze down at it through the window. 'It's a stratus cloud,' my mother says, reading from her phone. She tells us about thermal inversions and bodies of water; facts that float reassuringly on the surface of things.

'It's Beira's veil,' my grandmother says.

My mother has rented the house for Christmas. I go upstairs and leak onto the pillow.

'The scenery is beautiful,' my mother says, standing at the door. 'Why don't you go outside and look at it?'

'I can see it fine through the window.'

'It's not the same.'

'It is to me.'

I turn my head away; I am leaking.

'Call a plumber,' I say.

She doesn't smile.

I listen to them move around downstairs, their muffled voices. I prefer it upstairs. Downstairs keeps filling with water and being upstairs is like breaking the surface and sucking in air.

I float on the rented bed, scrolling my phone for stratus cloud facts.

*

'She has one eye,' my grandmother says at lunch, 'as cold as ice.'

'Mmm,' I say.

'Her teeth are black as soot.'

I frown. 'Sorry, who?'

'Beira. The queen of winter.'

'It's a lovely day,' my mother says.

Suddenly a terrible smell fills the air and my grandmother gazes into the distance. The shower runs. I can hear their voices echoing in the bathroom.

'Is it time to go home now?'

As I pass by the door my mother is peeling off the soiled pants.

'No, Mum,' she says. 'We only just got here. Why don't we go out for a drive and look at the scenery?'

My mother's need for us to look at the scenery is so strong that I have to kick against it to stay afloat. I stand at the window and look at the stratus cloud.

*

Facts, facts:
Stratus clouds do not precipitate.

*

My mother stands at the bedroom doorway jiggling the car keys. 'Why don't you come?' she says. 'It's a lovely day.'

'She has one eye under her veil,' my grandmother shouts from downstairs. 'And skin so withered and old.'

I shake my head. I am leaking again. Who could contain so much water?

The front door closes, the car drives away.

The stratus cloud hangs over the water. A deer stands in a neighbouring garden, its antlers spread like vast bony wings either side of its head. Its breath clouds the air.

I pull my boots on and crunch along the grass outside. I imagine lying down, pulling the icy grass over me like a blanket. The deer has gone.

'I just want you to land,' my mother told me once. 'Can you not just land? You're like an aeroplane that keeps taking off again each time you start a descent.'

'Maybe the aeroplane likes flying,' I told her. 'Maybe the aeroplane doesn't want to land.'

The mountains frown at me, dusted in snow.

I imagine drifting high above them, above the loch, the stratus cloud. The deer a tiny red dot on the white earth.

As children, my grandmother and her siblings were hidden in the freezing fields at night, so the legend goes. It was safer that way. When my great-grandfather came in, he drank, and when he drank he burst into flames. He couldn't help it: the fire was in his blood and his blood was in the land and the land was not his own.

It had been this way for generations. He came from a long line of fires: the bonfires lit at Samhain to herd the cattle through, the flames carried thrice around the house sun-wise at midwinter.

The drunken fires that raged all night.

*

'I don't live here,' my grandmother says.

'Me neither,' I say.

My mother taps the pencil against the newspaper. 'Endure. Seven letters.'

'Tolerate?'

'That's not seven letters.'

'Is there a letter?' my grandmother asks. 'Has it come for me?'

'It's the crossword, Mum.'

'What word?'

'The *crossword*.'

Outside the window, snow weaves drunkenly through the black air. 'Old Beira is milking her deer,' my grandmother says.

'*Weather*,' my mother says. Her pencil scratches across the paper.

'Beira pounded the frost into the earth,' my grandmother says. 'With her magic hammer.'

'Do you want a cup of tea, Mum?'

'And she created the mountains and valleys with the rocks that fell from her giant creel.'

'How about some *Songs of Praise*?'

Water starts to fill up my ears, their voices are muffled and far away.

'The loch was an accident, though. It was her maiden's doing, that silly wee Nessa.'

'Night,' I say, standing up.

'But it's only seven,' my mother calls after me.

I stand at the bedroom window into the black night. Someone whistles from outside and a dog barks distantly.

When my mother was a child she told me she used to hear my grandmother slamming doors and banging drawers upstairs. The slams and bangs were saying something, but what?

It was a fit of silence.

She told me it used to be so cold in the house that the bedroom floor would frost over. That if she stood on it with bare feet her skin would stick to it.

In the corner of my mind something is burning. I close my eyes and leak onto the pillow.

*

Facts, facts:
Stratus clouds are unstable, transient in nature.

*

'I live there,' my grandmother says, pointing at a passing mound of rocks. Then her face clouds over. 'It's cold out here. But we can't go back in just yet.'

'No,' my mother says, glancing at her in the rear-view mirror, 'not just yet.'

'But he'll be asleep soon, I expect.'

'Yes, soon.'

'Aye. Asleep in the chair. By the fire.' My grandmother stares grimly out of the window. I stare out of my window too as we begin to drive around the loch.

'Shout if you see the monster,' my mother says.

We don't reply.

'Just look at that sky.'

Silence.

After a while she swerves into a lay-by and jumps out, leaving her door open, beeping. She pulls my grandmother out of the passenger door and tugs down her trousers just in time. The wee runs along the road.

'Look at the mountains,' my mother says. 'Glorious.'

I get out of the car and crunch along the shingle. I crouch down at the edge of the loch and plunge my hands into its icy water.

My mother watches me as I walk back. I wipe my face.

'There's no monster in there,' I say.

'He's sleeping,' my grandmother says. 'During Beira's reign everything must sleep. Wells must be capped, duty must be obeyed.'

The car is still beeping.

When we get back to the rented house, the fog starts creeping in. Outside the window, ghostly shapes emerge from a thick white blanket.

'It's hard to see in a fog,' my mother says, looking at me. 'It's hard to see the scenery. The mountains. The beauty of things.'

Happy people are singing and dancing on TV; some old Christmas musical.

'Beira likes the cloud,' my grandmother says. 'It conceals her haggard face. And as the icy wind blows she cries I am weary and old!'

'Shall I turn the TV up a bit, Mum?'

My grandmother begins a wobbly dance around the floor to the music. Then her face hardens and she slumps back onto her chair.

'He's been gone a long time,' she says.

My grandfather was violent when my mother was a child. He'd drink and just burst into flames. He couldn't help it, the fire was in his blood and his blood was in the war and the war wouldn't let him go.

'It was a different generation,' my mother told me once. 'You know, in those days children were seen and not heard.'

My grandmother refused to speak to him for months on end, years even. Her silences were legendary. I remember visiting their house as a child and looking in their bedroom, the two single beds side by side with two little tables.

'It's sunny tomorrow,' my mother says. The musical has finished.

'Night,' I say, standing up.

My grandmother reaches for my hand.

'Never send a maiden to do a hag's duty,' she says, gazing up at me through her boozy lens of dementia. 'For the well will run and run uncapped and what will happen then?'

I am leaking.

*

Facts, facts:
Stratus clouds are more closely related to fog than other types of clouds.

*

The mountain path is slippery as I walk along the mountain path, a sheer drop to the loch below. My breath fogs the air.

It was my mother's idea. She came and sat on the edge of the bed. 'Why don't you go and commune with the mountain,' she said.

'Mountains don't commune.'

'Of course they do.'

All the trees are bare, except the pine trees, which jut out with spiky outstretched branches. I imagine drifting weightless above them, all my water gone.

Along the path, some children are playing.

'I will be Beira,' the little girl says. She picks up a tree branch. 'Beware, my sharp wand of winter!'

'What'll we be,' one of the boys asks, shivering.

She pulls her shawl around her and looks over at me. 'We can't go back in just now,' she calls out.

'No,' I say, 'not just now.'

'But he'll be asleep soon, in the chair.'

'Yes,' I say. 'Soon.'

A distant dog barks. I crouch over a frozen puddle. It has concentric lines like a fossil.

*

'In the days when the world was young,' my grandmother says, 'Beira saw land where there now is water and water where there now is land.' Food sprays out of her mouth and onto the table.

'And she was always followed by wild animals, old Beira,' she says, chewing. 'Wolves howled to greet her. And she charmed all the deer to keep them from the huntsmen.'

'After dinner we can finish the Christmas crossword,' my mother says.

My grandmother frowns. 'What word?'

'The crossword, Mum.'

'I don't have a cross word to say about anything.' She stares moodily into space. Candles flicker on the table.

In the corner of my mind something is burning. A drunken man raging at me on the street, sleet in my hair. Street lights blur. Broken glass crackles under foot. I back away, then I turn and I run and I run and I do not stop running. Then I'm waiting in a room no bigger than a broom cupboard. My trousers, pants, socks and knickers are in a box next to me. A nurse opens the door and hands me a paper gown. I put the gown around my waist. I have no choice, I tell the nurse silently. I have to set it on fire, all of it, just to make sure it is gone.

After the fire, the rain.

I push my plate away. I am leaking.

'Night,' I say, standing up.

'But you haven't even opened your presents,' my mother calls.

*

Facts, facts:
The lifetimes of stratus clouds vary depending on the type of cloud.

*

My mother stands in the doorway, fastening her coat. 'We're going down to the Christmas service, why don't you come?'

I shake my head, without looking up from my phone. 'Did you know,' I say in a tight voice, 'that the word "stratus" comes from the Latin meaning to stretch or extend?'

She sighs violently.

'You know, being in the middle of you and my mother is like being wedged between two obstinate boulders,' she says.

She's the best violent sigher I know.

I lie there, listening to the door close, the car drive away. I swim around the empty house sitting down on the sofa, standing up again. Staring out of the windows. My ghostly reflection stares back at me grimly in the glass.

I pull on my boots.

I walk further this time along the mountain path. Past great swathes of dead heather; iridescent gold, tangled in ice. The burn trickles down underneath it all, hidden from view.

I find a big stone and sit on it.

I gaze at the pine trees, their spiky outstretched arms. The loch far below, reflecting the sky. The trickle of the burn. Something lifts.

I hear a dog barking. It runs towards me. Then its owner arrives, out of breath.

'He doesn't like strangers,' she pants.

It looks more wolf than dog. 'What breed is it?' I ask.

'He is not used to strangers,' she repeats. 'He can smell you on the path.'

The wolf-dog growls.

'I'm staying in a house down there,' I say.

'Oh, that rented place. It's just there for tourists.'

I want to tell her my ancestors worked this land, that I am no tourist. That it holds their blood and bones and toil.

'We have a good view of the loch,' I say.

The woman nods. 'I remember it when it was a small round well,' she says. 'But that was a long time ago and I have long ceased to count the years.'

She calls sharply to the wolf-dog, who winds itself contritely around her legs.

'A well?'

'Aye. My maid Nessa used to cap it for me, with a boulder. One day she was so late in capping the well that when she arrived its water was overflowing. It was running so fast that she turned and ran for her life.'

The wolf-dog begins to whine and the woman scratches its ears.

'I saw her from my mountain throne, like I see everything. Very well my girl, I thought, from now on you shall run and run and never leave water. And so I turned her into the loch and that is how it came to be named.'

She digs at the frozen puddle with the heel of her boot.

'Sometimes I hear her sing her lament,' she says. 'It's a bonny tune, I'll give her that. You can hear it rising from the loch, as clear as a bird, as sweet as the pipes of fairyland. *Shush*, I tell her.'

The woman looks at her watch.

'I better be going for my lunch,' she says. 'Turkey, all the trimmings.'

*

We stare at the unveiled loch through the window. The stratus cloud has gone. Where has it gone?

'High concentrations of atmospheric carbon dioxide can cause stratus clouds to break up and disappear,' my mother says, reading from her phone.

The food steams on the table. My grandmother is wearing a lop-sided paper hat she won from a cracker.

I remark on the scenery, on my walk, and my mother is buoyed, she thinks I am coming in to land. After all, it is my duty to land.

I imagine circling high above the loch, descending slowly, the water stretched out like a long, lonely teardrop.

'If a loch could speak, what would it say?' my mother says.

My grandmother answers in the old language; we don't understand. The words hang in the air like ancient decorations.

This story was inspired by 'Beira, Queen of Winter', in Wonder Tales *from* Scottish Myth and Legend, *by Donald Alexander Mackenzie (Glasgow: Blackie & Son Ltd, 1917).*

Lynn Davidson
JUNE 2019

On an EasyJet flight from Edinburgh to Berlin the young man beside me is reading the score for Jonathan Dove's *The Passing of the Year*, song cycle for double chorus, two pianos and percussion. He is conducting as he reads. He's wearing shorts, a teeshirt, and jandals and has a thick beard. The creamy pages strung with notes lie open on his broad lap. His hands swim in the currents of the music. I try not to move, in case he stops doing what he's doing. I just turn my eyes towards him and watch. The piece opens with an invocation:

Oh earth re-turn Oh earth re-turn Oh earth re-turn
     Oh earth re-turn
Oh earth re-turn Oh earth re-turn Oh earth re-turn
     Oh earth re-turn
Oh earth re-turn Oh earth re-turn Oh earth re-turn
     Oh earth re-turn

The music dips and rises and then holds still in the air, he holds it there with his fingertips, so he and I and the notes, the double chorus, the two pianos and the percussion are suddenly paused, a single kestrel hovering in place with the opal earth laid out beneath it, until with a swoop he frees us to run back into the thickets of ourselves.

FROM SCOTLAND TO NEW ZEALAND

I sit on the shore
recovering from this

long breath-held dive to get here.
The shudder of relief
to breathe in air.

Such air in this place   the river of wind
between   these islands
lands
here and   here and
here

Less breathing in

material

Less breathing in material.

How to measure land-loss against
the gentle constant of breath.

I have left Scotland – the word, the place –
the way we move through each other like light through
            water.

Infrastructure will not solve distance.
Nor can you build a country inside another country.

However – a word that sounds like a river of wind
between islands – *however*

the word *bridge*, its excavating consonants,
its failing reach,
sits deep in the gullies of my mouth.

Lil DeThomas
THE GREEDY ALGORITHM

Red brake lights and I'm choking on my seatbelt,
on family reunion, headed to Santa Anita racetrack.
My cousin looks prophetic, though no one notices
there's a clot on the freeway, sea of cars scabbing up.

Of course my family romanticizes the gambling part.
My cousin belongs in the hot sand and can't sit still.
The sun got stabbed and bled through the windshield,
then we all got out to see horses running for their lives.

I see him walking to the concessions, he looks like Jesus—
like forty days in the desert—he looks like he could confess
but I know he won't. He looks at me analytically, like
he looks under the hood of his car, investigating something.

People walk the perimeter of the fence, and they wish
themselves jockeys, going faster than the LA freeway
where lane jumpers weave through the car mob. 'The
greedy algorithm pushes them further behind' explains

my cousin, the prophet. 'The cars that stay in their lane
move faster.' Maybe you should've driven, I think. But
he orders a slushie instead. When he drives he palms the
stick shift hard, sucks the gasoline dry—
gets what he wants by divine right, maybe.

When we leave the racetrack, we don't leave him behind
like I hope we will. There is hardly any room in the back.
My legs curl up like a snake as he gets comfortable.
I am nearly kneeling before him.
Kneeling before an atheist
that begs for forgiveness.

Shehzar Doja

A SEQUENCE OF LOSS

I.

If there is a sequence still left preserved,
I'll set a reminder to myself of the forensics of not
losing memories instead
of the canonical

sifting into the lungs of this abridged where I enter
past sundaes and the occasional
temper of a halo sold into transience. I sell photocopies
of these notes, scrying with synapses turned grey.

Here, the flowers unspring themselves.
Melanges a waning leaf into কাল বৈশাখী [1] *rain.*

II.

There is a template for losing
words, one slurping into the next
as the axial degenerates.

I describe it no longer
as a fog.

III.

There is a boy who looks

obsidian laced,
seizes skeletal
frames and wishes for more. He is replaced
into a refurbished memory.

---

1   Kal Boishkhi – a heavy torrential rain taking place across the Indian subcontinent.
Translates as 'Fateful thing'.

IV.
I am blending expired flowers
into my চা[2] this morning. The leaves distance themselves.

Yes, they distance themselves.

V.
Tapestries bleached to sense-
less ness. Blended mosaics to stir
memory, they stir stilted
gaps I have
yet to form.

There is a sequence
to discover I know
and fold for another
time.

---

2   Cha – tea.

Meg Eden
FAMILY DINNER

At the Eagle Lodge in Okinawa, we ate dinner at the
        dinner table.
All three of us, a family: together at that table.

In Okinawa, my father never stayed late at work. He
        drove us
around the island, talked with us while we ate at the table.

At home, my mother made a plate for him and left it in
        the fridge.
If he ate with us, he'd get up half-way through for work and
        leave the table.

When my husband and I rent a room at the Eagle Lodge ten
        years later,
we pick up Indian food and bring it upstairs to the very
        same table.

How do I explain that this is why I loved this stranger of an
        island, this
brief apartment building: all because of one lousy table?

In high school, my mind remained in Okinawa. I hated
        America: its lack
of manners, recycling bins, and good rice; its social rules,
        unstable.

I played sanshin music through my headphones; I wore geta
        on the bus.
I called Okinawa home, mistook an island for my
        dinner table.

When I was in high school, my father flew there every
        other month.
I counted the days 'til he'd get home, dreaded calls that
        said he was unable

to come back on time, delayed another week. Now, I
        come here
as if looking for him, but all I find is an outdated apartment
        with a table.

My husband and I eat here, watch the ocean's Ferris wheel
        light up.
My husband is always here – firm and solid like a table,

I can rely on him. He comes with me to all my favourite
        places:
Ryukyu Mura, the aquarium, the shops in Mihama, a
        buffet table

of my past. But my father is not in these places; he's back
        home
at his office, doing what he must to put food on the table.

And I've begun to forgive him for this, for how selfishly I've
        loved him.
The ocean says: *Meg, go home and be at peace*. My husband
        cleans the table.

Ellen Forkin
HARE, BEE, WITCH

I never profited the neighbours' milk, my familiars sneaking in the moonlight, with cream on their snouts. I have no poppets, dirty wax, torn linen and stolen hair, moulded with swift fingers to the likeness of my enemies. There are no spare pins to prick agony into them. I did not curse the village cat, plump and thick-furred, until it vomited up blood and lay on its side, all a-twitching. It was unwelcome upon my table, but I meant it no harm. I have lived many a year; I fear the rumours about me will live longer. But it is not true. I, Isobel, am good.

It has started to rain, a fine drizzle made ice by the wind. My body is tied to a stake with peat, and what little wood they can spare, all stacked up about my bare feet and legs. It will burn slow. I am in a shift, grubby and torn, my exposed body shivering violently. A crowd stares; surely the whole of Orkney has come to Gallow Ha' to watch. They take in my matted hair, unwashed skin, blooms of bruises, red, festering cuts and sores. My nose is broken, crooked. I am one of four women, all equally ragged and bleeding and staring into nothingness. We have known horrors. The executioner stands by, legs apart, breathing deeply. He, with a twist of rope in his meaty hands, promises of more horrors to come.

'Witch!'

'Hag!'

'Crone!' All shouted into the wind. Am I a witch as they say I am? I certainly didn't curse Old Rob who ate and drank too a-plenty, until the great redness of his nose and cheeks finally poisoned him. Now he is confined to his bed with only weak ale to wet his trembling lips. I am not homeless, dirty, and simple like Margaret who begged constantly for alms and bread and sometimes the sweet oblivion of honey. She slept in byres and barns, unseemly on folks' doorsteps. And neither am I like Ingrid, with her one, wandering eye, who has lived through many a bad crop. She was foolish enough to comment her wisdom on dying grain before the young folk even thought of the word 'famine'.

Oh yes, people are hungry.

I feel their eyes eating us up.

My throat feels prickly, exposed to the icy rain. Soon the rope will curl around my neck. A kindness, some say. A kindness before the flames. It is but little comfort. The meaty hands fidget, making the rope twitch.

After the strangling, our bodies will be burnt to nothing. We will not crawl out of our graves, groaning and undead, to torment the isles with our evil. On Judgement Day, we will not rise with every other soul, facing east into the holy light. That's what burning is: a precaution for the living; a punishment for the dead.

We will be unmarked ash, filth in the breeze, and nothing more.

I hear Margaret keening.

I try to twist to catch Agnes's eye. Agnes who is pious and good and churchly. Agnes who I, in my agony under 'the boots', named as a fellow witch because she was so devout. Who could ever suspect her of devilry? But then, it was Agnes who dared to scold the bishop for misquoting the Bible. Agnes who shamed her husband for not compensating young Jamie, his future uncertain with a mangled hand. Agnes who stood tall in church, singing loudly, unflinchingly. Untouchable.

The husband stands apart but does not look sorry. The bishop, I'm sure, is word-perfect now. The sermon and its prayers flow over us and few pay attention. Certainly not I.

My neighbours say I cannot recite the Lord's Prayer without mistakes peppering my speech. It's a tricky thing to learn for a simple woman such as myself. They say, in breathless whispers, that I slip out into the darkness as a midnight hare. To gaze at the moon and read the stars. They say I eavesdrop at their doorways as a bumblebee, then fly away home heavy with their secrets. It is common knowledge I killed the plump and thick-furred cat because she was a rival witch.

Shapeshifting. But not quite. I swallow, my throat raw, and think of my mother. Her murmured words. Her tricks. I gaze at the crowd, waiting, waiting. Anne, kind but slow, meets my eye. I strike.

Our souls – they swap. I snap into her plump and doughy body, taking my thoughts and feelings and knowledge and memories with me. Her blood feels warm and sluggish. Her fingers thick and shorter than I am used to. And my body, the one I have just abandoned, starts screaming.

'You've got the wrong woman! I'm not Isobel! I'm not Isobel! It is not I.' The crowd titters, delighted. Anne, trapped in my old body, sobs. Hysterical, ugly tears. The executioner wraps the rope around his hands. He is ready.

I step away. My new body has small, spongey feet. I cannot be Anne for long. I do not want her husband. Her children. Her skills of midwifery. Anne will be found lifeless, crumpled in a ditch, before the sun has set. The shock of the burnings, many will say. No one will notice the froth of hemlock upon her tongue.

And I will crouch in the heather, heart skittering, a midnight hare. My long ears twitching in the wind, as a flea bites my shank. I will hide and know that I, Isobel, am good no longer.

Timothy Fox
NOBODY REMEMBERS THE BIRDMAN

granny says he lived two doors down where the empty lot is

be quiet says the nurse *stop that fuss*

but granny points a crooked finger toward the window
he's out there carrying his house on his back
feathers falling from beneath his coat

Roshni Gallagher
MY GRANNY DREAMS OF GUYANA

My granny looks at me and she sees herself.

Her living room full of glasses – half drunk.
Pictures of gods hang above the bed. She listens

to a record spinning out in another room,
        another house.

                The rant of rain on begonias.
                Mangrove and wood slats. The parrot's asleep.

Things change.
I try to pull quiet in to cover us.
        The walls sing.

She looks at me
and she sees herself
        in the slant moon,
        the water,
        the waning bank.

Rodge Glass
ON SPECULATION

After *Dept. of Speculation*

1.

At the start of May 2020, I started buying books again. Books for me. Books for courses I'd be teaching online come September. Books recommended by friends and colleagues. Some dog-eared, some loved, some with unbroken spines. At forty-two, having just left half a library behind in my old office, unable to take so many things north to our delayed new life in Scotland, I was already building up again from scratch. Sometimes I'll say to C.R., It could be heroin. Or gambling! Or affairs! There are *definitely* worse men out there. Addiction is a big word, compulsion smaller. Either way, I've given away a lot of books over the years. Then set about gathering them up again, right away, as if the world was running out of print.

At least this time I wasn't acting in desperation. I wasn't parked on double yellows outside Oxfam on Byres Road, emptying boxes from the boot of my car out of spite. I did that once, in a rush. Dumping box after box between stops in the shop doorway to hack at my arms. 'Are you sure?' asked the young volunteer, as I turned to go, running a hand through her green fringe. 'This is, like . . . a *lot*.' Signed books, books I'd loved, books I'd annotated, books I'd studied and taught, books from friends, books *written* by friends – Dear R, With all my love; Dear R, Thank you for everything; Dear R, If you ever give me away I'll never forgive you! – the car was heavy, then it was gloriously, horribly light. I sat in the driver's seat and inspected my swollen arms. I reached for the inhaler in the glovebox, then started the engine. As I flicked the indicator, trying to get on the road before being caught by the advancing traffic wardens – oh for fuck's sake! – the trickle became a rush. Back then, I was too embarrassed to look at my all-too-recent life, so pretended it wasn't there. This meant getting rid. All these years later, I sometimes go to my new shelves looking for something, then realise it was part of a long-ago giveaway. At one point, just before moving out of the old place for good, I piled old volumes of this and that on the street outside the flat M and I had shared, along with various bits of furniture, fittings and God knows what else. A neighbour came downstairs and asked what on earth I thought I was doing, young man. I had no answer for her. I couldn't even pretend.

I've loved the short story 'Why Don't You Dance?' by Raymond Carver for years. At the start of it, a man pours himself a hard drink in his kitchen, while looking out at the old bedroom suite he and his wife shared during their marriage. The suite is now sitting in his front yard. He contemplates the nightstand, also the reading lamp on her side of the bed, or what used to be, now made absurd in its new public spot. The same nightstand and lamp are replicated on his side, each of these things lying, like a dare, for anyone to pick up as they pass. The only line of the second paragraph of the story reads like this:

'His side, her side.'

You can do a lot in a few words. More, if you give it space on the page. Now, when I think of my fire sale back in 2012, I feel I must have been the man in 'Why Don't You Dance?'. Looking crazy. Sounding high. Encouraging passers-by – young, loved-up couples at the start of their lives – to pick up my past so I could hurry along, unthinking, into any kind of future.

I've been starting again for decades. Escaping different schools, then England, Judaism, Israel–Palestine, friendships, England again, relationships, communities, jobs, and now England once more. But there comes a point where you aren't entitled to a clean slate any more. You can clean parts of it, cover other bits over. You can unburden yourself of things you own, telling yourself it's charity.

But the past is the past; it's what the present is made of. And there's no way to deny the past.

2.

When books started arriving at our home last May, the children got excited. Magic! Through our own letterbox! Sometimes I let L, our older girl, open the post herself. Sometimes she got to it first, running to her room with a whoop, squirrelling the treasure in some faraway corner of her room. Other times, C, our younger girl, opened the post with me in the hallway. I'd watch her face as she looked at the newly revealed cover of some strange, darkly scribbled crow, muted illustration of mussels, bleak-looking farmhouse or abstract painting. All before looking up at me with eyes wide saying, 'A-maaaaay-zing!' Some of these were books I didn't know anything about. Their authors were authors I'd never heard of. Sometimes I even forgot what I'd ordered them for, and in some cases I didn't know if I'd ordered a novel, or a memoir, or a collection of stories. I didn't know what I was reading. I had few expectations. In a sense, it didn't matter what I was reading. Only that when I was reading, I wasn't in the world.

One of the first to arrive was *Dept. of Speculation* by Jenny Offill. After ripping it from its bubble-pack envelope with my help, C rubbed her hands back and forth across the jacket. The image was of a blue sky that looked like it had words floating in amongst clouds so spare they were barely there. 'Like it, like it,' she said. I asked, 'What do you think it is?' She opened it at the title page and handed it to me, saying 'Lookdaddy, lookdaddy, a book!' Then she sat down on my lap, ready for story time. I was thinking about something else. I kissed the top of her head and put it to one side, then reached for *Pip and Posy: The New Friend* by Axel Scheffler, which was lying close by on the floor. 'We love Pip and Posy, don't we?' C is a toddler-sized megaphone. 'YEEEEES!' she yelled, and the package was forgotten. 'Pip and Posy were going to the beach,' I began, 'They unpacked their things.' Just then, C spotted Posy's favourite cuddly toy hanging out of her beach bag. 'Awwww!' she said, hugging herself before stroking the picture. 'Frog's a wee CUTIE!'

Pip and Posy can be relied upon, time after time, to deliver. Here is the plot entire of *The New Friend*.

1) Pip the rabbit and Posy the mouse go to the beach. They collect shells, dig a hole and paddle in the sea.

2) While Posy naps, Pip meets Zac the dog. Pip and Zac have so much fun playing together that they wake Posy up.

3) Posy is invited to play, but isn't sure. If Pip has a new friend, will he want to play with her anymore?

4) Pip, Posy and Zac go and buy ice creams.

5) As they're handing over the money, a seagull swoops down and takes Zac's ice cream. OH DEAR! POOR ZAC!

6) Posy gives Zac her last coin so he can buy another one. He thanks Posy and wipes his eyes.

7) They all walk happily down the beach, ice creams in hand. Posy suggests they build a huge sandcastle together. And they do. HOORAY!

Joy! Pain! Friendship! Kindness! And a happy ending too. In a parallel world, I'm invited onto *Desert Island Discs*. On arrival at the studio, I reject the traditionally proffered *Complete Works of Shakespeare* in favour of *The Complete Pip and Posy*, insisting on this swap as a condition of my participation in the programme. Naturally, the producer agrees with a smile. Her kids love Axel Scheffler. Meanwhile, back in the real world, I hugged C tight then stood and picked up my new package. As C had done, I stroked the front cover, already absent-mindedly thinking of something else as I climbed the stairs.

Around that time, though books were always arriving at the house, most of my reading was reading with the children. That, or reading about HHT.

3.

When I began *Dept. of Speculation* a few weeks later, I noticed what C had seemed to be showing me when shouting *lookdaddy* – that someone had written a note on the inside. Spidery writing. Not exactly clear. But clear enough.

> *MAY 2017.* To the 'I' of you, Lucy. So that you will learn
> to trust me again, and yourself completely. With love. From—

Then one more word. Jen? Jan? Jon? Let's call you Jon for now, I thought, leaning in on the page, edging closer and farther away, closer and farther away, like a magnifying glass trying to focus on a bug. The handwriting suggested more of a Jon than a Jen. It was a man's hand, I was sure of it. The scrawl of someone who knew others would have to work hard to read their writing, and yes actually they were fine with that, what of it? The book's epigraph was from Socrates. 'Speculators on the universe . . . are no better than madmen.' I don't know why, but I snorted – enjoying the sensation of briefly, ever so briefly, feeling superior to Socrates, maybe? What did that guy know, eh? Doesn't he know we're *all* speculators? Whether we want to be or not?

That night, I had so many things I was avoiding doing that I didn't know what to do with myself. While wandering between rooms, picking toys and clothes off the floor after the children were in bed, I spotted my copy of *Living with HHT* by Sara Palmer on the windowsill. I hid it under my desk, feeling vaguely sick. In the weeks since Joshua's birthday I'd kept returning to that book for answers, though of course no answers were in it. Just medical language, and pictures, and the stories of people whose lungs were strong enough to make it through a single day on their own. When trying to concentrate on, say, blood vessel abnormalities or how diagnoses are made, on diagrams or on personal testimonies, I was doing what I do best. Highlighter in hand, I thought about how both the Hebrew and Christian calendars seem to work hard to multiply the anniversaries. Or rather, how they multiply the opportunities for remembrance. Of Joshua's life, his death by HHT, in spite of the odds – and what that's made of us all.

Each year, there's his birthday. That's number one.

In 2017, Joshua's year, March 26th was a Sunday, Mother's Day no less – so there's Mother's Day to mark as well, whenever that falls. His mum is always his mum, whether he's alive or not. That's number two.

Then there's number three, the Jewish Yahrzeit, which starts at sunset and is marked by the lighting of a single candle and the saying of a prayer. Ner ne'shemah, it's called – soul candle. Number three usually falls a couple of weeks either side of the end of March, dependent on the movements of the moon. So far, so Jewish. But there's more.

On the Shabbat of the Yahrzeit week, there's also number four – an annual mention of Joshua at synagogue, which we're always invited to as well. It's never a cursory mention. The other anniversaries they list are mostly of people who lived long lives, some of which ended long ago. They're remembered by children, grandchildren, sometimes by the wider community. Jews never mark things once if they can get away with it, that's the old joke. Though when the rabbi talks about Joshua's mum and dad's response to his short life, his long legacy, I can't laugh. No synagogue this year of course, even that's going online now. The rabbi, front and centre in his living room, a couple of his younger children like mini hype-boy and hype-girl, either side of him, the boy battering an improvised drum between his knees while his sister dances and claps along to the prayers. Reaching out through the screen with their smiles, as dad tries to summon the old community spirit through the unifying power of Zoom.

Living with HHT was published after he was born, after he died. It didn't even mention Joshua by name. What I'm saying is, *Living with HHT* didn't stand a chance.

Certain places in the old house have become frozen in time. Standing at my bedroom window, I remembered – how long ago was it? – when I stood at the same spot and apologised to my sister-in-law for what happened to Joshua, while looking out onto the park behind our house. 'I want to take responsibility,' I said down the phone, 'for what I didn't do,' though of course it was too late to do anything, and the apology was as much about what I needed as anything else. Joshua is her baby, but she was trying to make it easier for me, which is the measure of her. She said she didn't blame me – though she did, if I remember rightly, say the word 'acknowledge' at one point, the word 'denial' at another. Words can tie knots, but we both know. That all this could have been avoided, had I only looked after my own health, and thought, just a little more, about those around me. You can spend decades hiding in stories if you like. Stories can change lives, they can even save lives. But none of that changes what's already happened in the real world.

As I sat there looking out at our garden, the metal drum in next door's garden slowly eating up hunks of wood in a smouldering fire, C.R. was downstairs talking to a friend. I could hear her laughing through our paper floor. I popped downstairs and saw a bottle of wine had been opened. Good, I thought. I returned to the bedroom, took *Living with HHT* back out from under the desk and hid it again, this time above the wardrobe. Sometimes you can't put a book far enough out of sight. Then I picked up something I wanted to read, tucked my feet into the duvet and hit the bedside light.

4.

The start of *Dept. of Speculation* is split into lots of short paragraphs, with fat margins and as much white space on the page as text. I like that. It makes you feel like you're racing towards the next thing, whatever the next thing is. At first though, the story was disorientating. It started with something vague about antelopes and vision. Then something the narrator thought about the nature of memories. Then it moved to an anecdote about a time when the narrator was travelling alone and hid a raw steak in her purse, loath to leave the thing, bloody and unwanted, on her plate. The narrative soon cut again, sharp, to a time this same woman spent in a French park, pretending to read Horace. 'In Paris, even the subways are required to be beautiful' is how the line went. I didn't know what was happening, but I'd been sold since the word 'steak'.

Jon had left the first page unmarked, though by the second he was already getting involved. The next line after the one about the subways of Paris was in italics, being marked with two stars. 'They change their sky, not their soul, who run across the sea.' Was Lucy supposed to know what Jon meant here? Was it something to do with trust? On the following page was a short paragraph about a summer when it rained and rained. In every city, said the narrator, the scene was the same: 'A boy stepping into the street and opening an umbrella for a girl keeping dry in the doorway.' To this, Jon had added '(Oxford Street, everyone . . .)'.

I might as well have been reading the Cyrillic alphabet. I looked at this comment for a while, dumbly. Then shook my head. So little of what a reader experiences is what a writer intends them to. What hope did Jon – not even the creator of this book, a mere whispering onlooker, a bug in the eye – have of controlling Lucy's experience? I thought about the last time I was in Oxford Street, which made me think of London, which made me think of my brother, which made me think of Joshua Jonah Glass, who lived for three hours and who I never met because, because, because. All books lead to Joshua, not just *Living with HHT*. One way or another, they do.

By Chapter 2, Jon was warming up.

At the phrase 'they put it through anyway', Jon ticked the line.

At the phrase 'Life plus structure equals activity' he wrote 'useful'.

Page 7 read 'For years, I kept a Post-it note above my desk. WORK: NOT LOVE was what it said. It seemed a sturdier kind of happiness'. At this, Jon had underlined the last seven words. Adding 'Read "Scaffolding", a poem by Simon Armitage'.

So Jon was giving Lucy homework now, and me too. This was the first time I thought, No wonder Lucy sold the bloody thing on! In these circumstances, it suddenly seemed like the onlooker was the one with all the power. What chance did the author have of cutting through all this chatter? I opened a new tab, huffing audibly. I typed in 'Scaffolding Simon Armitage poem'. Disgracefully, the poem did not immediately flash up before me, so I put *Dept. of Speculation* down and put out a call. One reply read 'Do they mean "Scaffolding" by Seamus Heaney?' By this point, I was down a hole. I found Heaney's 'Scaffolding' and took a photo of it. It's a poem of one simple metaphor: the construction of loving, enduring walls.

Poor Jon, I thought. He thinks his betrayal will be forgotten because he built a wall, way back when. I forgot I had been looking for another poem; I became distracted by the hope that Lucy might start answering back. We never went to Oxford Street, did we, Jon? Must have been your ex-wife, that one. No, I won't read what you tell me to. No, I won't forgive you, Jon. Leave me alone. LEAVE ME THE FUCK ALONE.

Back in May, I was working from a small make-up desk in our bedroom. I was especially preoccupied. With the ever-burning drum next door and the sound of threats at all hours. With Joshua's recent anniversaries. With my many conditions and never, ever feeling well. But despite all that, two people kept finding their way back into my thoughts. Lucy and Jon were now real to me. Every bit as real, at least, as my brother's rabbi, his smiling children in the screen, my own past giveaways, and the characters in *Dept. of Speculation*.

5.

As it progressed, the structure of the book became clearer. Some of these short paragraphs were fragments from the early days of a relationship history between a woman and man, shown from the woman's perspective. Some sections were related to memories, or moments, or things that stuck in the protagonist's mind, though it wasn't always clear why one thing stuck while another didn't. The connection between the different strands of the book wasn't always immediately clear either, but I built up a picture of the narrator as the pages passed.

'The wife', she called herself. It matters what you call yourself, right?

Page by page, Offill seeded what her narrator did for a living and how her relationship with 'the husband' evolved over time. The years before and after marriage, before and after the loss of a pregnancy, the birth and growth of a serious young child. The pages are sprinkled with wonder and the protagonist keeps reaching for quotations by others. For Jon, this was a gift. How could he resist the urge to point at, to highlight? On an early page, Jon had underlined this italicised sentence *'Remember it is possible to feel this way'*. Perhaps he hovered over the words, wondering if Lucy would intuit what he wanted her to, even without his annotation. But what if she missed what he needed her to see? Some risks you just can't take. Every comment was a mystery to me, every underlining a question. I closed my eyes and tried to imagine Jon, or Jan, or Jen. The curve of his jaw. Her face, in profile.

"On Speculation" is an extract from a longer essay.

Heather Gregg
SHAKEN

w, f
so   all
n

k   q   i
li e   u   e
t

f   e   t   e   i   w   h
a t r   h   p l o f g t
l   i

n   h
i   t i s

e   e
up   nd d

go   g v   e   a   se o   e
l be   i e m   p u   t   fe l

h
t e   li

gh t,

se tl
t   e

Kris Haddow
THE INCOMER

You came intae the bit and got brandit an incomer. Bounced intae the Big Club fu o flair and panache. Hair slicked back oer yer shouders, made up tae the nines. Ye carried yersel wae a confidence that marked ye oot fae the get-go. Sly glances passed atween folk. Strangers in toon, twae guid luckin lassies at that. Lik Twiggy and Jerry Hall. Hips got leant intae, elbows touched as ye's jostled for space tae request yer Malibus and Tia Marias and sic like concoctions. Wee Josie ahin the bar had a field day diggin the bottles fae oot back, made a show ae presentin them tae ye's baith for approval afore yer drinks got poored, fair prood o hissel as he mixed them. Must hae money tae burn, folk thocht oot loud. No that ye's paid for owt. Ye's were weel seen tae that nicht, miner's strike or no. Better than the local lassies, much tae their chagrin. You and yer pal danced wae onyb'dy that asked. Ye's even had the cheek tae dae the asking! The Big Club hadnae seen the likes afore. Talk aboot brazen! Fellas' eyes were drawn tae ye's. Lassies' eyes were drawn aff ye's. Auld Missus Harkness and Aulder Missus Campbell were scandalised, lips pursed, erms foldit, whispers fleein atween them. Somehin michta been said aboot hoorish skirts and cheap hussy beads and durty floozy face-paint. The young farmers fae Auld Kelloside were fair took wae ye's, wae baith the look and the likes ae ye's. The men fae the pit stood affronted roon the wa's, feet shuffling, pints clutched tae their chests. The boys' faces beamed bricht red like skelpt erses if ye went onywhere near them and said *hullo, ye fir dancin, then?* Every man in the bit wis besotted wae ye's. Wae you in particular.

You came intae the bit and got talked aboot for weeks. That incomer that showed hersel up at the dance yon Saturday nicht, wheelin and flingin hersel aboot the flair wae Big Jock McClymont. No that onyb'dy kent where ye were fae. Ye just wurnae local, no fae roon here. Stood oot like a sare thumb among the Peggies and

Nancies and Jessies and Ags. Stood oot fae the folk that grew up here. Funny tae hink that yer pal got forgot aboot. Richt enough, she wis back mony a time aff the bus fae Dumfries tae stert wae, ay when there wis a dance up the Big Club, or the times when there wis a band booked for the pub. She rarely stayed oer or went wae ony fellas, at least no that folk kent o. Would hitch the main road early hours efter shuttin, went wae lorries or vans or cattle wagons or cars. Nae care in the world for who picked her up at stupit o'clock. Folk here seemed mare worried aboot her than she wis aboot hersel. No that ye seemed tae gie it much thocht. Ye'd done it yersel often enough. There wis a wee distance stertit showin atween ye's efter a while. Noticeable. A seat apairt at the bar as she blethered tae Wee Josie oer a drink, less enthusiastic for the dancin while you got aa the attention. She stopped appearin efter a while yince ye settled wae Big Jock. It wis soon efter that that yer pal wis forgot.

You were an incomer yet when ye took McClymont's name in the February, rushed as it seemed, or so folk said. The banns were postit but were suitably vague. Still nae notion ae who ye were really or where ye were fae, just that a Mr and Mrs O'Toole were pleased wae the announcement o their dochter's betrothal. An appearance wis made by the aforesaid at the waddin. Irish soundin, folk said. The minister kept schtum aboot whither ye'd been Catholic or Protestant afore signin the kirk roll, but sign it ye did, and just like that, yer name wis enshrined. Big Jock seemed richt pleased wae himsel, a braw bit lass like yersel at his side. And soon – overly soon, some said, if ye thocht aboot the dates – ye'd put a wee skelf o a lassie in his airms, and no too lang efter that, there follied a wee bit boy tae play at his ankles. Iona and Andy, ye's cried them. Holy names, Scottish names, traditional yet modern at the same time. A happy wee brood ye's made. Even as the last o the pit jobs were wound down and Jock landed work on the railways, ye's still ay seemed happy as the weans waited and watched and waved from the sidings as the great diesel engine roared back intae toon. Big Jock'd swing doon, and he'd scoop them up, and smother

them in kisses, and they'd roar and laugh and bury their happy
wee heids in his oxters.

You were still gettin cried it as the decade turnt and a third bairn
filled yer belly unexpectit. Queer that, sic a gap syne the first twae,
and wae Jock ay away. Some o them pointit oot ye'd ay been like
yon wae yer unsettled ways. Kept yersel tae yersel, the incomer up
the hill. Iona seemed tae be confined tae kickin stanes roon the
garden o yer auld pit lodge, wee Andy skippin school on the regular.
Folk said it wasnae natural, the weans skitin aboot like that, you
knockin aboot the hoose aa day, yer man away fae the bit sae often,
they weans no gettin looked efter. Folk wunnert if yer wee surprise'd
be rid-heidit like the first twa, or whether Jock'd be a stranger to
it when it shied oot the womb. It wis said, efter aa, that yin ae the
Douglases fae the Byre had tane an awfy interest in fixin the shed
up by yours on the auld pit road, that he ay got a piece or a blether
at yer door when he chapped. It gave folk ideas, stertit rumours
gaun roon. And it wasnae the first o them either. Auld Missus
Harkness on the widows' alms row – drawin her curtains early tae
watch the news as Thatcher waved her lang oerdue adieus – had
said nuhin as the boy Douglas again crept by wae a shifty gait; she
did nae mare than *tsk tsk* a month later when she'd spied him at
dawn. It wis nane ae her business, she mindit, though she wis ay
quick tae inform Missus Campbell by phone. The shed was scarce
roofed, and the winter drawin in when the Douglases had upped
and flitted. And that, mooths flapped, wid be the end ae that.

You were the worst sort o incomer. Yer cairds were marked. Not
once had ye set foot back in the kirk oer the years. Ye hadnae joined
the guild, or the rotary, or the boolin green. Ye'd been asked on
the gala committee, but ye never wrote back. It wis weel noted, so
it was, that ye were a rank outsider. Even the weans wurnae appearin
at school. Thocht ye were suhin special, some said, up there on
the outskirts luckin doon on the rest o us, leevin aff Jock's wage,
him worked tae the bone. Less spring in the big fella's step as he
lowped aff the last train fae Carlisle or Newcastle or Warrington

or Crewe. Further and further oot the bit the work had tane him. Less sign ae the bold mannie that asked yon braw lassie for a dance at the hall. Sic a sorry sicht tae see him staun there unmet, a weary weight on his back as he'd brace hissel for traipsin that brae, silverin heid bowed, tae what folk imagined wis a cauld lonely bed.

You were a sorry luckin wummin when they put him in that cauld, lonely grave. Yer hauns on yer taught belly, Iona at yer back. *Awa too soon*, folk telt Big Andy, the boy havin streetched, staunin there luckin his faither's drawn spit. Nae denyin that yin. *Man o the hoose*, they kept sayin. The last ae Jock's relatives made the pilgrimage fae Fife. *Sorry for yer loss, a bloody thing, the cancer, a richt shame.* Folk had forgot that Jock wisnae local, wis an incomer hissel, had come for the graft doon the pit when the wee toon wis thrivin.

You were pitied for a while. Folk would see ye sat on the bench up the brae, luckin forlorn doon the glen where the trainline wended. Doon the way Big Jock had went for the work. Back the way ye'd first come in fae way back when. Folk said ye'd smile and say *hullo, how ye daein* as they came and went. And well dammit if folk didnae manage a wee bit beam back and say *fine, how's the wean.* For ye'd the Silver Cross pram at yer side on yer dauners, wee Jack he'd been cried, a bairn wae sic fiery a heid o hair the likes ae which'd ne'er been seen. *He's grand* ye'd reply, *wee smiler, like his faither.* Jist like his faither.

You gret at the station years efter when Big Andy enlisted. *That's the lassie McClymont's boy awa tae Cattrick*, folk said. Mare Jock's double since he'd turnt sixteen, a muckle broad stock o a lad, wavin his faither's auld cap oot the windae as he'd left. Iona fair prood o her big-wee brither, the twae o them daein weel in spite o they hard years they'd had, and her newly turnt seventeen and engaged and in love. Wee Jack crashin doon the platform on his bike squealin *byeee!* till the train took the bend and wis finally gone.

You howled on Iona's waddin day next spring an'aa, happy tears tae be sure, the mither o the bride, o that braw skelf o a lassie newly turnt eighteen. Wee Jack the page, fair smert in his suit, lovin aa the attention, folk sayin *ye luck jist lik yer da*, poor Wee Jack no kennin ony better as he'd ne'er got tae meet him. A wee shame tae that Andy hadnae made it. At the tea, the minister wis seen smilin and noddin as ye's blethered at the purvey, pickin at the pieces and the sausage on sticks, and ye were seen tae be thankin him and sayin *aye, aye ye wid*. And afore folk kent it, ye were weekly in the kirk and arrangin the flooers. And ye'd soon joined the choir, *a lovely wee voice*, the Young Miss Campbell was sayin. She'd first heard ye sing at her auld mither's funeral, and again at Missus Harkness's the July efter. Ye'd gied her yer condolences, but been shocked at the reply. *A richt pair o auld craws* she'd joked at the wake, and ye's had stifled yer snorts and yer laughter behin hankies as ye's dabbed at yer mascara as it stertit tae run.

You were sat in the tearoom on the main street the Monday efter Jack left for big school – fair proud o yer boy, ye were – when a van drew up and parked across the road. A couple jumped out, and ye'd sort ae kent the fella's face, and the lassie seemed happy as larry as they'd opened a hoose door, and he'd fussed and fawned and tried tae lift her oer the stoop, and ye'd grinned as ye watched them and they vanished inside. Wee Josie broke yer reverie, sayin *hullo, how's it gaun*, an auld man gettin now, but still his same cheeky self fae the days in the Club. And you said *aye, aye ah'm grand, Josie, just whilin the day awa*, and he nodded and he asked *did ye spy love's young dream, then* wae a wink and a shrug o the shooder tae the van oer the street. *One o the Douglas fellas, moved back wae a bride*, and as ye smiled in recognition, Wee Josie said *his brither woulda been a friend o yours a while back, wis he no . . .?* and he left the question sort ae hangin there.

You saw the folk sat nearby crane their necks tae lug in. But still ye smiled as the face finally fit, and yer eyes seemed tae sparkle, and ye said *Aye, he wis indeed, Josie. Yin ae the few that understood, that asked when ah wis – well, ah wis no weel. Couldnae cope. He was a guid man. Guid neebors, aa the Douglases.* You looked fondly across at the van and the hoose, and Wee Josie wis awfy affronted, his face bricht scarlet as he realised he'd oerspoke. Yet ye took his haun in a rare show ae affection, and ye said *Here, it's fine – ne'er heed, Josie. Ah ne'er have.* And he grimaced, and sighed, and that wis as close as ye'd be gettin tae a sorry for aa the years folk roon here had misjudged ye, had miscried ye. And fae then on as word got aroon, it came tae pass that folk thocht ye mibbe wernae sae bad, efter aa.

You took a great slug o tea. *Mrs McClymont* Josie said wae a tip o his cap, and as he made to walk off, ye asked *Whae's the new Mrs Douglas, onyb'dy ye ken?* wae a gesture oot the windae tae break the tension in the air. *Och, ah dinnae ken,* he replied. *The Douglases hae been awa fir a wheen o years, sure. He'll hae brocht the lassie up fae doon south.*

You felt somehin then. You kent that she'd come intae the bit and get brandit an incomer. Kent that yince they got stertit, she ne'er stood a chance.

You kent it, but ye didnae hae tae like it.

You nodded tae Wee Josie, said *ladies* tae the rest, grabbed yer purse, and coat, and ye stood, and left.

Nat Hall
HAIRST

Feel da mareel.
Noo da licht leaves wis aa alone, wi
da mirkin creepin early,
da last o' da Simmer gone ta rust.
Atween da nicht an da moarnin,
A meadow pipit i' da girse
hentin da morsels laek a thief afore

                        da next gale, hellery –
an i' da eens o' October, whaar
da cloods hang ta TV masts,
da dark blue licht o' da
moarnin is
yet ta leave wis fur da sun.
Wir hairst reminds wis o gansies,
Da need ta wipe oot da windaes –
hear da sistimus i da stanes,

                  da innerdaeks o wir ain world,
bricht callishang,
      spaekalation ahint da glass
                      juist afore eight, as
staris gadder apö da wires . . .
Telegraph codes in
languages
      da Hairst records an understaands.

Shetlan Glossary
da Hairst: Autumn; **da mareel**: phosphorescence in the sea (algal bloom);
da Simmer: Summer; **da girse**: the grass; **hentin**: getting;
da hellery: storm, adverse weather; **da eens**: the eyes; **gansies**: jumpers;
da sistimus: wren: **da innerdaeks**: the stonewalled area of a house;
bricht callishang: very boisterous vocalisations, noises;
spaekalation: rumours; **ahint**: behind; **staris**: starlings; **apö**: on

Alan Hill
SAYING IT LATE

For the first time
I told my mother, aged ninety-two
that I love her.

'That's good dear', she
replied.

The conversation shifted.

Twenty minutes on
she told *me* something I had
never heard

of the joy, indescribable
complete
she had had in April 1965
on a late spring evening
in a small country hospital

as she bore witness
to my first breath, I made
my first sounds, arrived.

Alex Howard
COUCHSURFING AT NIKOLAY'S

He met us at Kyiv station,
its crematorium-like archways
filigreed with gold,
its Soviet escalators
lapping like tongues of steel.

We had walked past him, twice:
his calls drowned
under the brakes of trains
that squealed like the victims
in a slasher horror.

He led us through a park,
Chernobyl swings dangling like nooses,
and through a Brutalist underpass
grey and dead as graphite.
Here I uzed to play viz mother,

he said, brow lumped like tyre tracks.
At his flat, he poured us vodka
turning on all three bars
of an electric heater,
that glowed orange with the dust-

singed scent of irregular use.
Six shots in and he's nodding at landmarks
from his ninth-floor window,
eyes sparking like flint
in the city's sulphurous glow.

All evening long
his war stories splintered and fell
like Panzer-struck birds.
The next morning, we slink out early
saying we have a flight to catch. Untrue.

At the underpass, I stared back at his block:
a ribbon of starlings
performed optical trickery
against its sun-shocked brick.
They're the only life I remember.

Shane Johnstone
MOCHEIRIGH

Dhèanainn mocheirigh
mus biodh glasadh air an là
dh'fhàgainn cuirp srannail
mo mhnà 's mo leinibh
agus choisichinn a dh'obair
ann am marbh a' gheamhraidh
tron bhaile mhòr fhàsach.

Ged a loisgeadh an sgìths
anns gach ball-bhodhaig
bhiodh m' aire air a ghlacadh
le guthan Saoghal na Gàidhlig
am fònaichean-cluais' a' chlàradair
ris na dh'èistinn gu dlùth
air an t-slighe uamhraidh.

Bhiodh iomradh soilleir Màiri
a' tarraing uisge faisg air Càrnan
ga mo thoirt air falbh
bho fhàsalachd na maidne
Ò ach gun tarrainginn-sa
à tobar ann an Uibhist
seach gròsaireachd ghrannda
à làraidh mheirgeach Shainsburaidhs.

Ghabhainn farmad dian-ùidh
ri sgoilearachd Meg Bateman
shaoilinn gun robh a h-eòlas
mar fhreumh na h-eanchainn
a' cur taic ri faclan iriosail
fon ghlac mi èiginneachd

a b' aithne dhomh 's a bh' orm
ach na freumhan a dhìth
sin a shaoilinn san dol seachad
air na togalaichean neo-chleachdte
agus sgudal grod càrnta
air an robh mi mion-eòlach.

Chithinn m' anail ceòthach
mar a dh'ath-aithrisinn air cainnt
Choinnich Mhòir 's Alasdair Ruaidh
air ruitheam 's blàths an còmhraidh
gun glacainn criomag dheth
san dol thairis air an drochaid
far am falbhadh an trèan.

Ruiginn am bùth mòr an sin
na for-uinneagan fosgailte
agus mu dheireadh thall
bhiodh an là air glasadh tharam.

Chuirinn asam
na fònaichean-cluaise
chluinninn eòin a' bìogail
agus crònan garbh
na làraidh-lìbhrigidh
ghabhainn m' anail
agus bhiodh obair là
a' tòiseachadh.

Charles Lang
GOOD FRIDAY

After Edwin Morgan

Three o'clock. Yer hot cross buns ur in the oven
fur another nine minutes. The soup will be tested at some point
the mora, or maybe oan Sunday. The world is oor oyster!
There'll be nae eggs this year fur a few reasons.

I press play oan the telly: a recordin ae Tuesday night's
       Eastenders
preceded by the last minute n a hof ae Tuesday night's news.
That feels like such a long time ago. The days aw feel the same
but everythin is movin quickly. I fast forward through the
       theme tune.

Ian is feelin guilty fur the part he played in Dennis's death.
Blackmail is a wonderful thing. Dotty is usin it tae take control
       ae the Arches.
Will Sharon ever find oot? Will Mick sell the Queen Vic?
Did Carole Baskin kill her disappeared husband n feed him tae
       her lucrative tigers?

These ur things ye need tae think aboot. The questions
that need tae be answered. Is it possible tae eat mer than three
cream crackers withoot a drink a watter? How many days
will it take me tae complete this 1000-piece *New Yorker* jigsaw?

TBC. Maybe I'll dae it the mora, maybe I'll dae it next week.
Tell ye wit I'll get most ae it oot the wiy the mora, efter ma soup,
takin a break at aboot three o'clock fur a wee coffee.
The hot cross buns, by the way: outstandin.

Len Lukowski
SITES OF HUMILIATION

Cairngorms National Park, now

We strip off our clothes to swim in the loch, shrieking as we plunge, water so icy, we feel reborn. Skin chapped from the cold, bodies dripping, we lie on the banks laughing from the shock, freely showing it all off – the scars, the fur, the incongruent bodies, not afraid.

Shivering, I rub a towel against my body, wrap it round my torso. Invigorated as I feel, I've no desire to get back in. You can't get enough and return to the water before your skin's had chance to dry. I watch you swimming, graceful and fast, you remind me of an otter. I take a picture with my phone, instinctively attempting to check Twitter afterwards, no reception. A moment of frustration before I ask myself what the fuck I'm doing. I'm glad there's still a physical world of beauty away from the pantomime of online discourse. I'm glad I found a person with whom I can be flawed and real. The sun is coming down when you emerge again. I've put my clothes on, they're clinging to my damp body. You come to me all cold and wet, push me on my back and climb on top of me. I grab your majestic arse with one hand and, though the midges have already begun to descend, put the other between your legs.

Reading, then

Eight years old, in the cloakroom outside the classroom door, the place we all get changed after P.E., I find myself naked. I took off my kit, about to change back into my uniform but my underwear was sweaty and stank of B.O. so I took it off too, isn't that what you're meant to do? I'm always getting confused. Classmates, now fully dressed and either sitting at their desks or loitering near me in the cloakroom start to notice. Laughter and commotion rise. Mrs Brown is sitting at her desk, I can see her from the door, she catches sight of my naked body and begins to smirk. She calls the remainder of the class in and they obey, except me, I stay where I am, not making a move to put my underwear back on lest it's a trick. 'Come in here now!' she shrieks. '*Now!*' I stand to the side of the door so the wall shields my nakedness, poke my head around. In a rage she takes to her feet and marches towards me, grabs my arm. I try to pull away but she's bigger, pulling me forwards to her desk. She parades me before the class who have stopped laughing and taken on the kind of earnest facial expressions only children can muster as they watch and wait to see how the punishment will progress.

Cairngorms, now

After we've fucked I lie on my back on the grass, arms around you, rubbing your body, trying to warm you up. The sun has gone down and the midges are feasting on us but I do not want to move. I crane my head back. 'Look!' I whisper. Something is staring at us, its shadow looming large. Deadly still behind us, watching, is a stag.

Manchester, then

By the time I am thirteen we have moved cities three times for Dad's job. Each time I'm relieved. I never really have friends at school and I imagine that, in the new city, things will be different. I won't get bullied, I will be accepted, loved even, by my peers, I won't fight with my parents, maybe I'll have a boyfriend. Each time I am crushed. Walking into every new classroom I am greeted with a chorus of laughter and 'Is that a boy or a girl?' 'What the fuck is that?' Much as I try to look and act like I'm meant to, I can never crack the code. But there's some freak blip in the natural order of things just before my thirteenth birthday when a popular boy at my school, Peter, befriends me for some unknown reason. We go to a theme park with my family for my birthday and Peter comes with us. The theme park is near where my grandparents live so we drop in on them after. My grandmother greets us with a customary

European kiss on either cheek, including Peter who is stunned at such a violation. She proceeds to embarrass me by speaking to my father in Polish. I watch Peter's eyes widen in horror, praying she'll shut up. My granddad remains on the sofa watching TV. But even the TV is a source of shame – he is watching the Polish channel. My grandmother makes bigos, smiling generously as she serves it, Peter looks like he's going to throw up.

'I don't like your family,' Peter tells me after dinner when we're both standing on the stairs thinking we're alone. 'I mean, I like your mum and dad, but not your nan.'

'She's just weird because she's Polish,' I explain desperately, trying to cling to my short-lived rise in social capital. Once the words have come out I feel another presence close to us and turn. My grandmother is standing in the doorway to the front room, watching, pain in her face like I've punched her. I feel a knife twisting in my guts.

The natural order is restored at school the following week, any brief spell of protection Peter's friendship granted me is more than made up for when he tells the whole school of my freakishness. Nobody usually gives a shit about the Polish thing because I was born here and a weird surname in itself doesn't mark you the way the Black or Asian kids or the first generation immigrant kids get marked. What hurts is the memory of her face.

Cairngorms, now

I wake to you snoring beside me. The ground is bumpy and I'm sore but somehow feel I've slept well. The sun is up. I look at my watch, it's just after six. I crawl out of the tent, the grass is wet. I squat down and piss, staring at snow-peaked mountains in the distance. A sip of water makes me realise how thirsty I am and I find myself gulping down the whole bottle. I love the mornings, especially out here, where nothing can hurt me. My brain hasn't begun its daily ruminations yet and I haven't looked at my phone and anyway there's no signal. I reach out my arms, like some daft hippie, revelling in the space, lay on my back, stretched out on the grass like a crucifixion. There is no past, no future in this half asleep state, no families, no world to hurt us, no history to scar us. I say 'us' but in that moment there isn't even you. My eyes take in the white dots of distant sheep against lichen-green mountains.

Paris, then

Streetlights illuminate the rain before it lands on the pavement and evaporates. Me and Sarah are outside a club in a part of the city that is otherwise quiet and tired.

Sarah never used to drink much before she met me. The first time I came round to her house she offered me a choice of tea or water. I had to work to hide my outrage. Now we're always getting drunk together. Sometimes we'll be drinking red wine at ten a.m. 'I love you,' Sarah tells me outside the club. I don't answer. I want to love her but I can't. I keep her around as a distraction, I can't say that either. Her telling me she loves me makes me angry because it can't be true. I never tell her anything about myself, our whole relationship is built on lies.

'Yoshimi Battles the Pink Robots' is audible from inside the club. Sarah's face drops into a sadness that almost breaks me. 'Sorry,' she tells me.

'Don't be sorry.' I hug her because I can't think of what else to do. I can feel her crying. I close my eyes and fall into the embrace, I feel like crying too. From somewhere in the darkness a bunch of teenage boys begin laughing, shouting, '*Gouines!*' I pretend not to care.

Cairngorms, now

Hikers are confused when they see us. We're both in our thirties but mostly read as teenage boys, such is the experience of trans men, particularly as neither of us are on hormones. I was on testosterone for a year before deciding it wasn't for me, but that was a while ago and, though I care less now than I used to, on bad days going back to not-passing is pretty mortifying. You dabble occasionally, but haven't for a while. When we speak our voices, though deepened from our time on T, have reverted somewhat and come out at a higher pitch than most hikers expect. When we exchange a friendly 'hello', many look alarmed.

London, then

Me and Kris sit on the back of the N29 – two depressed gay zombies. Around us Halloween clubbers gay and straight, returning from Soho, scream at each other, having mock fights, laughing loud, abrasive laughs. The congealed glittery red blood dribbling from my forehead is slightly peeling. 'You guys look great!' a tottering fag hag informs us, waiting for a reaction to appear on our gay zombie faces, confused when it doesn't. 'Oh well, take care yeah?' she says, crashing into the seat behind us.

I was the one to spot the skeleton. 'Let's take him home!' I shouted to Kris over the music, uncharacteristically confident on MDMA and in need of constant stimulation to match my buzz. I was under no delusions that Kris should approach first, but instead of securing a threesome, as was his mission, I found him in the gents with his zombie cock out, the skeleton on his knees. Kris was trying to be quiet, but his muffled grunts were unmistakeable. I won't deny it was hot watching as I waited for them to notice my face above the cubicle door as drugs and rage and arousal pulsed through me.

Eventually Kris threw his head upwards and opened his eyes. '*Uh!* I . . . hi . . . we were looking for you.'

The skeleton stopped what he was doing and looked up, gesturing for me to join, 'Come on babe, I like girls too'.

'I'm not a fucking girl,' I snapped, losing control of my voice 'til it reached a shrewish pitch, like a nagging wife.

The skeleton looked confused.

'You can't have it both ways,' Kris tells me when we're in bed after what seems like an eternity on the bus. 'You want an open relationship but you don't want me to do anything.'

'Not when we're out together.'

'You suggested it!'

'I suggested a threesome.'

'I know. I was just . . . laying the groundwork.'

'Fuck you.' I roll over and move as far away as I can.

Cairngorms, now

'What are you laughing at?' You're fiddling with the map, taking so long to open it.

'Sorry, you just look really cute.'

'Because I can't read a map?'

'Because you can't open a map. *I* can't read a map.'

'Aye, you can!' You fold the map back up and toss it at me.

As we walk, between companionable silences, we get into our usual topics: bitching about friends, lovingly of course, the queer scene and its many public fall-outs. Streams run through the valleys around us like veins.

Bangkok, then

I can't understand anything on the menu but it probably doesn't matter. I just want to get out of the heat, away from the crowds and traffic. I've spent most of my three days in Bangkok in my room, enjoying the air con. On the last day I force myself to go and look at the giant golden Buddha so my whole time isn't wasted. I'm covered in sweat and in a daze. After travelling for three months I've run out of energy for exploration. My T shot is overdue and I can feel myself getting fatigued and irritable. I hate my country but I miss my home. Back near Taksin Tower, close to where I'm staying, I shun the places set up for foreigners, thinking I am somehow not like other tourists. I go to a restaurant where everything is written in Thai with no English translation or western customers. It's a little room that opens out onto the main road.

A young woman sitting at a table looks up and addresses me and of course I don't understand what she's saying so I go for a greeting in badly pronounced Thai: 'Sawadee krap.' She looks at me with disgust. Shit, what did I say? 'Sorry,' I say in English. She doesn't stop staring at me with repulsion. It's at this point I realise the woman doesn't work at the restaurant at all, she has a laptop open in front of her and wireless headphones and is talking to someone on Skype. 'I'm sorry,' I say again in English, 'I thought you were talking to me.' Still she says nothing. Her expression of disdain deepens. A guy sitting at the back of the cafe bursts out laughing. It occurs to me she might think I'm trying to hit on her. I sit at a table and stare at my phone. Sometimes I look up towards the woman who is still eyeing me as one would a sex offender, I quickly look down again. I touch my sweaty stubble anxiously and wonder if I look like some sleazy white guy come to pick up young Thai girls. I feel a familiar twist of mortification. The staff ignore me. After thirty seconds I get up and leave.

Moray, now

You have a meeting in a nearby town tomorrow and need to shower – we planned the trip around it. We drive through country roads, mossy green mountains on either side.

You lie on one of the beds at the BnB we eventually find and I get on top of you and we kiss, too tired to fuck, barely enough energy to scratch our midge bites or prize our bodies from the cheap duvet.

Hackney, Columbia Road, then

When I arrive at the pub it's just Bridget and her new girlfriend. If I had any dignity, I would turn round and walk out again. I sit down. Bridget hugs me, I feel turned on. She introduces me to the girlfriend and I say hi as coldly as possible. Bridget's normy friends who have never liked me arrive. They look surprised when they see me, the time off T has softened my face, one of them 'she's' me, but Bridget puts a stop to that. 'Oh, I'm sorry,' normy friend says, 'I thought you'd . . .' I pretend not to hear. The friends like the girlfriend and nod earnestly as she boasts about her fucking activism. I sit by Bridget and there are moments during the evening when she's tactile with me, touching my arm or hugging me and I start to think, maybe she wants to get back with me. I am still sitting by her at last orders and the glint of hope is all that matters, that and the occasional brush of her fingers against my side.

Eventually Bridget announces she is tired and wants to go home. The girlfriend is going home with her, they live together. Fuck's sake. I walk though the rain to my bus stop, past bouquets of dying flowers.

Moray, now

'Special treat, is it?' asks the waitress in the dingy restaurant down the road from the BnB, eyeing our passports. She is a middle-aged, well-spoken English lady who immediately asks for ID when we ask for beer. Yours still has an 'F' and your deadname, but even after she's seen them the nice lady continues to address us as children.

We giggle once she's gone. *'Special treat, is it?'* we imitate. The only other patron is a man with a crumpled brown jacket and a big grey beard who looks like part of the furniture, motionless aside from the occasional lifting of pint to mouth. 'There we are,' says the nice lady, setting our pints down, smiling nervously as though we are intimidating, rather than a pair of soft faggot Sufjan Stevens fans.

A rowdy family group arrive. Three generations. No children. The 'kids' would be the ones in their early twenties, the quieter, more reserved ones. The oldest is a man who's maybe in his eighties and full of the joy of life, you can feel it as he walks in. They all seem pissed already, in a good-natured way. The lone drinker does not look up.

Our pints continue to multiply after our microwaved food has been eaten. You start going off on one, because we've been reunited with wifi, about some latest thing you've seen on Twitter: 'People are only interested in trans people if we're traumatised, sometimes I think it's a competition who can suffer the most.'

'Babe, the whole of social media is a competition for who can suffer the most.'

'Aye, I suppose,' you stroke your patchy sideburns.

'Sorry, young men! So sorry for the swearing! We're terrible here!' The old man from the rowdy table shouts over. We smile and wave his concerns away with limp wrists.

I philosophise drunkenly. 'I think I've led a pretty privileged life but actually the worst things that happened to me happened before I even knew I was trans. Being trans and queer made everything better because there was like, a community at least, a family outside the nuclear one.'

'What happened to you?' You're always trying to work out what the great trauma in my life is that turned me into such a trainwreck. Why I can't hold down a job, can't get through a night without a nightmare, can't get through a day without drinking, take two different types of antidepressant, have been hospitalised three times after breakdowns if you don't count the time I was in for the overdose.

'I mean, nothing really. There was no one big thing. My parents had trouble coping with stuff, with me, and we kept having to move 'cos of Dad's work, and then, just like mundane unhappiness. I mean I was bullied at school, but I guess that's normal. If you're queer.'

I feel embarrassed for not having more in terms of trauma, I feel like there's no excuse for being like I am. I know you grew up in harder circumstances, below the poverty line with an alcoholic father, though you always dismiss the idea you ever have anything to complain about. 'Spare me your middle-class guilt, babe! Other folk suffered far worse.'

Maybe some people just get broken down by little things. Tiny sites of humiliation that alone wouldn't amount to much, but chisel away at you gradually. I see in my mind's eye a kind of

Google Maps, each place where some incident of shame occurred marked with a star.

I feel a darkness rise in me. I guess it's the end of the trip, the facing of reality. I look over at the old man. He's not chewing over existential angst and he's probably been in wars and shit. Again he starts apologising to us for the 'colourful language' that peppers every sentence. Everyone at the table is laughing.

You go to the toilet before we leave and as I'm getting up to go the old man addresses me. 'Young man, I'm so sorry about this table! The language that's come out of our mouths this evening is just *terrible*.'

Drunk and emboldened I shout back, 'Not at all! It's fine!' That's when the table falls silent. Various heads double take me. My voice is clearly audible and does not match my body. I am a teenage boy with a thirty-something woman's voice. Most of them get over it, chatting quickly starts again, but not him. The old man's face is mortified, like an abandoned puppy. The family is talking about whether they should have more drinks but the old man does not join in. He stares at the empty space in front of him and keeps staring, as though frozen in time. And I think about swimming in the loch the day before and how it felt like being reborn but you never get to be reborn, not really. I watch him looking at the tablecloth like his greatest love just died, as if, just by existing, I ruined his life.

'Come on, babe.' Your warm hand takes mine and leads me out the door, but not before you stop and survey the rowdy table and the nice English lady, all trying not to look at us, smile, and shout, 'Bye folks!' in a way that sends startled shockwaves through them all. All except the lone drinker with the big grey beard who continues to lift pint to mouth, calmly, without fear.

Aoife Lyall
MATINEE

I talk to you like any mother would, about our trip away
the empty fridge, what we'll have for dinner. It's a script
I run from aisle to aisle, full of imminent birthdays, phantom
guests. *Flour. Sugar. Loo roll. Eggs.* You watch my words

mirror my lips, mouth *packet, pasta, sachet, dried.* Food
that just needs water. I make a show of forgetting, go back
for noodles, herbs, long-life milk. Things in jars, preserved
in oils or spices. Sweet things that will keep. And soap. And soap.

At the till, I libel your innocent father, make the house
both empty and a mess. I chat and pack the bags, plan
what to forget and when to come back. When we leave
I spin the trolley through the carpark, load the shopping first.

HAMPER

There is no wicker here, or straw: no delicacies or dainty preserves.
Instead, there are cardboard boxes and plastic bags filled with raw meat

and real butter, fresh fruit, and frozen bread. I collect it from a local hotel—
the one just past the crematorium where every other car turns off—

and do what I am told to do—*Do not arrive too early or too late. Reverse*
into the pick-up bay and wait, and someone masked and gloved will fill

your boot with the food you ordered at least three days ago. We do not speak
or touch—*keep your windows up*—or get close enough to see each other's eyes.

I like to think they're green, with flecks of grey that flicker blue when they drive
home by the loch. I like to think that someone knows for sure.

Hannah McDonald
JAM AND BUTTER

It was the first day of the summer holidays, and my best pal Francis and I were playing outside when it started to rain. It was a muggy, clammy day, a day just waiting for a downpour, crying out for it. When the droplets finally hit my arms they were almost warm.

'You can come into my bit,' said Francis. He smiled at me, his little milk teeth pocked with brown rot. I hesitated – I had never been inside his house before, had only heard the things my mammy said about it.

'Och it's a shame,' she'd say. 'They don't even have shades on the big lights.' She'd never told me directly not to go in, but her descriptions made me uneasy at the prospect of it.

'C'mon,' said Francis, already running away from me. 'I'll make you a piece.' The rain was coming down thick now, soaking me. I was apprehensive, but also a bit hungry.

'Awrite,' I said and ran after him.

At Francis's front door, we paused. He tried the handle but couldn't pull it down. He sighed, glanced back at me apologetically. While he braced himself and began shouldering the door, trying to force it open, I looked at it. The white paint was chipping off in places, exposing wood underneath that looked like it was rotting. I thought of my mammy, standing outside our own front door with a big rag and bucket, wiping it down every Saturday afternoon. My daddy painted it once a year, in the summer, to keep it looking nice and fresh. I tried not to look at Francis's door; I felt embarrassed. I wondered why his da hadn't kept up with the paint jobs and considered asking my own daddy to paint the Murphys' door too the next time he did ours. With a final shove from Francis, the door finally cracked open. He smiled at me triumphantly and led the way through.

The horrible old front door opened right onto the stairwell; I stepped inside and looked up to my right, as Francis ascended the steps to darkness. The window at the top of the stairs didn't seem to be letting in much light, and the stairs themselves were bare; no carpet, just wooden boards. There was a vague but ominous smell, like rancid chip fat, and the walls looked greasy, a dirty brown colour. I stayed where I was at the bottom of the stairs.

'Should I take my shoes off?' I called up to Francis. I heard him laugh, but didn't hear a reply. I closed the door gingerly behind me and made my way up the stairs.

At the top step I paused and peered into the long hallway, allowing my eyes to adjust to the lack of light. Francis was standing at the end of the hall, looking into the room to the left. He was talking to someone but his voice was quiet and I couldn't make out what was being said. Though his house was identical to mine in layout, it didn't feel the same as my house at all. I slowly made my way down the empty hall, pausing to peer into the open doors of the three bedrooms. In the first one, to the left, was a double bed held up with feeble-looking metal poles, covered in a single blanket. There were no pillows. In the second room, two single mattresses had been placed on the floor in different corners of the room. The last room, the smallest, had one mattress on the floor and a cot in the corner for the baby. Coats were strewn on top of each of the bare mattresses. At first I thought that Francis's mammy must not care very much about the weans making a mess on the beds, but then I realised – they covered themselves with the coats while they slept. The Murphys had nine weans; I hoped they at least had one coat each.

I continued down the hallway until I reached the end. To the left was the living room, where I finally saw who Francis had been speaking to. Mr Murphy was slumped down on the threadbare sofa, smoking cigarettes and listening to the radio. His undershirt was covered in tiny hairs of tobacco from rolling his own fags. Mr Murphy was a tiny, stringy man who always looked harassed. He'd get off the pit bus at the end of the day, covered in coal dust, and Mrs Murphy would be waiting for him at the bottom of the road, bursting to tell him all the terrible things the weans had done that day. By the time they got to their front door he'd be so wound up by his wife that he'd spend fifteen minutes leathering his children before he sat down to dinner. He looked up at me and I was immediately afraid; I had never looked at him directly before. But his face was soft, lined and pallid, his eyes small and tired. He smiled at me.

'Awrite hen,' he said in his raspy voice. 'You up here to get oot the rain?'

'Aye,' I nodded.

'Very good,' he said, sucking on his rolled-up fag.

'Daddy, can I make us some sandwiches?' Francis asked.

'Aye,' Mr Murphy said. 'But don't use too much butter. And make me one as well.'

Francis took my arm and turned, leading me through a door across from the living room and down a step to the kitchen. The kitchen was a big square room with counters all around and a table in the middle, an unoccupied pulley hanging from the ceiling. Dishes were piled up in the sink.

'Where's your mammy?' I asked Francis as he moved busily around the kitchen, grabbing supplies – a loaf of plain bread from the cupboard, a jar of jam from the pantry.

'She's staying at my Auntie Teresa's hoose. She's helping her oot because my cousin Peter's no well.'

'What's wrong wi him?' I asked. Francis didn't answer. 'And who's looking after all of yous?'

'Well she took the three youngest ones with her. The rest of us are old enough to look after ourselves.' I thought about this carefully. Francis went to the Catholic primary school but I knew he was in

the same year as me, primary six. I didn't think that was old enough
to be looking after yourself; I couldn't imagine my mammy leaving
me behind to go and look after somebody else's wean.

'Brendan had a fight with ma daddy last week so he's been
staying at ma gran's hoose,' Francis continued. 'Paul and Steven
are working in the pits now so they're out aw day, and then at night
they go and drink aw their money away in the club, as my mammy
says. And Julie does typing in a lawyer's office in the toon. She
says she's gonnae get married soon and then she'll get away fae
here for good.'

Francis had laid out all of the ingredients for the pieces and was
now pulling out slices of bread, inspecting them carefully. I looked
at the things on the table: the pot of jam opened, breadcrumbs
surrounding the loaf, a block of butter on a rectangular tray. It was
warm in the kitchen, and the horrible chip-fat stink was much
worse up here. The butter had started to go rancid in its grimy tray,
oily yellow liquid pooling around the solid cube like golden pus.
A fly landed on the lip of the jam jar and rubbed its hands together
greedily. Suddenly I wasn't hungry anymore.

'Francis, I think I hear my mammy shouting on me,' I said,
wanting more than anything to get out of that dank, close kitchen
with the peeling linoleum and rusty taps, the heavy air and the
stench of old cooking.

'What about your piece?' He asked. 'Give me a minute and I'll
make yours first; you can take it home wi ye. Look, I'm nearly
done.' So I stood there and let him make me a sandwich, putrid
butter scraped onto mouldy bread, covered with jam that a fly
had luxuriated in. He handed it to me and I looked down at it.

'Well, I'll maybe see you the morra,' he said. I looked from the
sad piece to his face and patted his arm for a second, knowing
that it was a strange thing for me to do but also wanting for some
reason to offer him physical contact.

'Aye. Thanks for the piece.'

I left the Murphys' house and ran all the way down to the burn in the rain. I thought about throwing the sandwich into the rusty, slow-moving water, but I was afraid someone would see me and give me into trouble for being wasteful. So I went to the woods further along the burnside and found a quiet place to dig a small hole with my hands and bury it. I plucked a leaf from a tree and placed it over the freshly turned earth like a flower on a grave. Then I went home for my tea.

Christopher Whyte
STARTING WITH A FATHER

> For I had a father
> ANNE FRATER

I.

If I had no memory of the moment when
I was forced to swallow my father's heavy sperm
till I was nearly fifty years of age,
is it something I need to be ashamed of?

Ashamed because my mind and spirit raised
a defensive wall around the horror to
prevent me being entirely wiped out?
I hear it, reaching me from every side,

your endlessly repeated plea to keep
silent about what happened, what I suffered.
"We do believe you! But, for Heaven's sake,
don't torment our ears with talk of it!"

If I show no pity, then it's for the sake
of so many children within reach
who suffer the same injustice today
and for the adults they'll grow up to be.

II.

I told the boy I was ready to journey
back with him into the past, and relive
the horror, the panic and the disgust
he experienced when his father raped him.

My words were generous and heartfelt, possibly
lacking somewhat in awareness, for
I imagined I would take him in my arms
so as to offer him comfort and strength

Crìsdean MacIlleBhàin
TÒISEACHADH LE ATHAR

Oir bha athair agam
ANNE FRATER

I.

Cha robh cuimhn' agam air a' mhòmaid anns
am b' fheudar dhomh sìol trom m' athar a shlugadh
sìos gus an robh mi còrr is lethcheud bliadhna
a dh'aois. Am bu chòir gu robh sin 'na adhbhar

nàire? Gu robh m' aigne is mo spiorad
a' togail balla-dìon mu thimcheall air
an oillt, air dòigh 's nach rachadh mo lèir-sgrios?
Cluinnidh mi, gam ruighinn air gach taobh,

ur n-agairt leanailteach, gum fan mi balbh
mu na thachair rium 's na dh'fhuiling mi.
"Tha sinn gad chreidsinn! Ach, mas e do thoil e,
na bruidhinn air! Na peanasaich ar clàistneachd!"

Mura bheil truas agam oirbh, tha sin
air sgàth na cloinne mun cuairt oirnn, glè fhaisg,
a dh'fhuilingeas an ceart eucoir an-diugh,
is nan inbheach a tha ri cinntinn asta.

II.

Thuirt mi don bhalach gu robh mi deasaichte
ri tilleadh còmhla chun an am' a dh'fhalbh,
gus fidreachdainn uair eile oillt, a sgreamh,
eagail an uair a dh'èignich athair e.

Bha mi a' bruidhinn air dòigh fhosgarra
is fhialaidh, beagan aineolaich is dòcha,
smaointinn gun glacainn 'nam ghàirdeanan e
gus cobhair 's neart a sholarachadh ris

while he protested and cried out aloud.
I forgot I was dealing with myself.
When I actually began to feel
what he felt then, as the adult I now am –

despair and horror overtaking me,
with no chance to escape, with not a trace
of any sort of help or comfort – I nearly
fainted at what he suffered and survived.

III.
Since I was a child, I've been afraid
of bodies, of my father's most of all,
given the disgusting opportunity
it gave him to corrupt and wound, hidden

beneath a sham of decency and morals.
My own body, however, filled me too
with fear and disgust, because it left me so
vulnerable – abject and defenceless.

If I didn't have a body, no one
could grab hold of me and do me harm.
So I perfected the perverted skill
of cutting myself off from my body,

observing it as if from far away
like an object in the hands of evil,
abandoned to cruelty and contempt
which had no chance of reaching the real me.

fhad 's a bhiodh e 'g acain is a' glaodhaich.
Dhìochuimhnich mi gu robh mi dèiligeadh
rium fhìn, agus an uair a thòisich mi
air fidreachdainn gu fìrinneach, 'nam inbheach,

an eu-dòchais 's na mhaoim' a cheannsaich mi,
do-dhèantachd an teichidh às, easbhaidh
gach lorg air cuideachadh no furtachd, thàinig
fanntais orm leis na dh'fhuiling 's sheas e ris.

III.
Bhon a bu leanabh mi, bha eagal orm
ro cholainnean, gu h-àraidh bho cholainn
m' athar, oir cheil i comas sgreamhail air
leònadh is truailleadh, còmhdaichte le tuar

na deusantachd 's a' mhòraltachd. Ach bha
mo cholainn fhìn a' cur sgreamh 's eagail orm
chionn 's gu robh i coireach air mo so-
leòntachd, m' easbhaidh dìon' 's mo dhiblidheachd.

Mura robh colainn agam, cha b' urrainn
do neach sam bith mo ghlacadh no mo chiùrradh.
Dh'ionnsaich mi leasan coirbte uime sin,
a bhith gam sgarachdainn bhom cholainn, mar

gu robh mi sealltainn oirr' o àite fad'
air falbh. B' e oibseact aig an donas i,
lìbhrigte ri cruadalachd is tailceas
a dh'fhairtlicheadh orra beantainn rium fhìn.

IV.

That might explain me toying with the notion
I actually belonged to a different species,
even if the people I had dealings with
reassured me I was just the same

as they were, something the members of
my family lacked the generosity
ever to acknowledge or admit.
I put on a show of being human,

it could have been a piece of clothing I
wasn't sure would fit me, fearing people
would laugh or jeer since I looked so peculiar
and ill at ease wrapped up in its folds.

I could only rejoice at my success,
astonished at finding them so gullible,
strutting around as if I could really take on
another person's manners and connections.

V.

What I am able to look on as "myself"
resembles a ghost that has haunted a home
for decades, stories about it passing
from mouth to mouth within the family,

among the people who came to stay with them
and others who count among their acquaintances.
Sometimes there would be no palpable sign
beyond the briefest shifting of a curtain,

IV.

B' ann uime sin, math dh'fhaodt', gum b' urrainn dhomh
tuairmeasachadh am b' ann do chineal eile
a bha mi buntainn, ged a bharantaich
gun dàil na daoin' a chunnaic mi mun cuairt orm

gu robh mi coltach riutha, staid nach deach
aithneachadh air neo cho-cheadachadh
riamh le buill cheacharra mo theaghlaich fhìn.
Bhithinn a' feuchainn na daonnachd orm

mar gum b' e aodach i nach robh mi cinnteach
gur freagarrach rium, nach bitheadh an luchd
ri gàireachdaich is magadh, 's mis' a' coimhead
cho mì-chiatach is amaideach fo phasgadh.

Bha 'n ro-chreidmeachd gam chur fo iongantas
's mi toilichte le mar a shoirbhicheadh
mo spaidsireachd, mar gum bithinn air modhan
is cleamhnasan neach eil' fhaighinn an iasad.

V.

Nas urrainn dhomh sealltainn air mar "mi fhìn",
tha e mar thaibhs' a bha tadhal air taigh
fad dheicheadan, is naidheachdan mu dheidhinn
a' dol mun cuairt, siubhal bho bheul gu beul

measg buill an teaghlaich, ach cuideachd eadar
na thug iad aoigheachd dhaibh is na bha eòlas
ac' orra. Cha bhiodh sanas eile ann
aig amannan seach gluasad goirid cùirteir,

or else a shadow passing through the room
without an object to be casting it,
or a gentle voice that reached you from
the other side of a closed door, and when

you opened it, there was nobody there.
Till a courageous girl encountered the shape
and proposed that it should tell her the whole story.
They took a seat. The ghost started to talk.

no sgàile siùbhlach am meadhan an t-seòmair
gun oibseact ann gu bhith 'na adhbhar dha,
air neo guth caoin gad ruighinn bho thaobh eile
dorais dhùint', 's nuair a dh'fhosgail thu e

cha robh neach sam bith ri fhaicinn ann.
Gus nach fhac' caileag mhisneachail an dreach
's na iarr i air eachdraidh choileanta innse.
Rinn iad suidhe. Thòisich e a' bruidhinn.

Liz McKibben
KNOWN UNTO GOD

One by one crofters down spades,
lock sheepdogs in sheds,
drag boats on to shores.
Sunday suits fall awkward on a weekday.
Thin shoes tread sharp on paths of stone.
One by one a knowing glance, a nod of the head,
A procession proceeds, silent, solemn.
No place for a woman.

Those who found him washed up on the shore are the first bearers,
not kith nor kin, not even on the same side but the dominie, ghillie
and the ablest of the unfit not called to war.
The coffin is solid, the corpse barely enough.
Mothers stand by doors, heads bowed,
hoping their sons may be spared this slow steady march.
At the fank, cattle grid and the loch side the bearers change in turn,
shoulders smarting from the old load or stiffening at the new
as the sailor shifts in his shroud.

At the graveside a skein of geese flies past
while respect for the dead hangs heavy in the air,
minds focused on those who will never know his body lies here
and hope for his knock at the door.
All the while the sheep graze on.

Jane McKie
ROPE

You told me the brightest flowers grow on sand.

By the breakwater, a frayed nest of fishers' rope
twined into a bouquet: pale blue, green, teal,
and peach; a twisted tale of what growth is.
But you are right – they are flowers in the way
of any weathered thing, unpicking itself,
or hollowing itself into something eye-catching,
essential: a split egg of rock, a breaking wave.

Hugh McMillan
COUPLE, NEW CUMNOCK

He's drinking strawberry hooch
and adding to it
from a green vial
like in a horror film.

She is half sleeping on her
handbag. They both look
about fifteen but my compass
is off on these matters.

The train is passing
New Cumnock, and he takes
his parka off to cover her,
even though she already

has a parka, and strokes
her face under a curl
of blonde hair
that seems carelessly

arranged but has taken
a hundred thousand years
of human evolution
to place in exactly that

heartbreaking manner
on her white cheek.
I want to say cherish
and take care,

but somehow it's like
a painting and I wouldn't
say cherish and take care
to a masterpiece

even though it has flaws,
so I watch them instead
poised like this
while the rain comes down.

Scott McNee
JELLYFISH

Characters

Kestrel – younger
Ridley – older

The sound of something slapping into a sink.
  The women's bathroom in a theme-park café. **Kestrel** *and* **Ridley,**
employees, stand at the sinks, one of which contains a dead jellyfish.
Kestrel *takes off her marigolds and drops them in another sink.*
Ridley *is cleaning the tiles.*
  Kestrel *chews at the fingers of her un-gloved hand.*

Kestrel I don't think it's infected, but it does taste like metal.
    Feels like I'm battering my teeth away here.
Ridley He didn't go through the windshield so much as the
    other way around. They told me it could have gone some
    distance if it hadn't hit the roof. Long-jump distance.

Kestrel holds her hand out for inspection. **Ridley** *doesn't look.*

Kestrel Is this scab or rot?
Ridley Remarkably clean cut though.
Kestrel IS THIS SCAB OR ROT

Ridley keeps cleaning.

Kestrel We can talk about my hand or your husband but we
    can't do both.

Ridley stops cleaning, inspects the hand.

Ridley It's a sting, they look like that.
Kestrel Does it spread? I think I swallowed some jelly gunk.
Ridley You're not supposed to eat it, but I think you'll be fine.

Kestrel Can I claim for this? You're not supposed to be getting
  gnawed by toilet jellyfish as a cleaner, right? Like I could
  sue?

Ridley I dunno. Customers will probably get first go at suing.
  My husband—

Kestrel You know, back in my Asda days they just paid out
  instantly, avoid all the bullshit.

Ridley goes back to cleaning.

Ridley Did folk at Asda get routinely attacked by jellyfish?

Kestrel Not when they were shitting. *[beat]* A robin flew into
  the store once.

Ridley That's not the same thing.

Kestrel If it shits on you though. Could go blind.

Ridley Did it?

Kestrel Did it what?

Ridley Sh— Mess on anyone.

Kestrel Nah, it just drowned in some Greek yoghurt. Had to
  throw it out.

Ridley I don't – what?

Kestrel Don't what?

Ridley How does that work? How and why?

Kestrel I dunno, someone must have opened the stuff earlier,
  left it curdling in the aisle. Wasn't really up to us to play
  janitor, so we left it. And then I guess it kinda looked like a
  bird bath, so the robin dives in, gets all its feathers glued up,
  dies. And again, I wasn't a cleaner back then, so fuck all to
  do with me. And then this kid shows up, and we're all just
  watching at this point of course—

Ridley Of course.

Kestrel And he gets all upset, like 'Mummy what's wrong with
  the bird'. She's too slow so he's already picked it up, before
  you know it, rubbing feathers, rubbing his tears away. She's

yelling, at him, us, about bird flu and shit, he's crying, the
bird gets dropped on the fucking linoleum. The janitor
finally shows up, sees all this. Crowd, dead bird, tears,
feathers stuck to a fat little kid's face. I took a picture. We
weren't supposed to have our phones on the shop floor
mind, so I got fired.

Ridley And rose to your current position.

Kestrel Yup. Always been my dream to scrub toilets with a
widow. *[reaches for phone]* You wanna see the picture? I
also have this video of a guy called Jamie, and he's got both
hands squeezin—

*The toilet flushes suddenly. The sound of blockage. Both women
straighten up.*

Ridley Oh dear.

Kestrel Can't be another one.

*She crosses over, looks down the toilet. Sighs, walks back over for her
marigolds, pulls them all the way up her arms. **Ridley** just watches.
Kestrel goes back to the toilet and pulls out another jellyfish, which
she sticks in an empty sink.*

Ridley It boggles the mind.

Kestrel I think they've been planted. As slander.

Ridley You'll be meaning sabotage.

Kestrel Slander-sabotage. To ruin the park. Maybe even
management! Some sort of Warren Commission type
cuntery. Like, they're so deep in the hole cause they built a
theme park about space but it's not the nineteen-sixties so
no one fucking cares and they're just throwing ideas at the
board, tryna sink us—

Ridley Or the world's falling apart.

Kestrel That one of the signs from the Bible, aye? 'And lo, the
sea did spew forth electric organisms up the shitter and
into Job's holy taint'?

Ridley I can take the rest of your bile Kestrel, there's nothing
    new there. But I'll not have you on knocking the Bible.
    There's better folk that have tried.

Kestrel 'Wherein Job's taint did pucker, and swell, and so
    expand that Job was unable to excre—'

*Ridley strides over, threatening. Both of them are interrupted by
the sound of a door swinging open, and turn to look off-stage. Loud
trumpet plays from off-stage.*

Ridley We were almost done, sir, but another one's just come up
    through the pipes there.

Trumpet blast.

Ridley Well, we could use another two or three folk helping . . .

Kestrel Yeah, Ridley's so old, sir. She can't hack it anymore.

Trumpet blast. They flinch.

Ridley & Kestrel Yes sir, sorry sir.

Door slams shut.

Kestrel Arsehole. He'd never have got away with that at Asda.
    [beat] I saw him on Tinder once, it was fucking
    embarrassing. Maybe we could get you on Tinder now your
    husband's crumped it.

Ridley I think I'm past all that.

They resume cleaning.

Kestrel Any non-religious theories?

Ridley Any non-offensive ones?

Kestrel Jellyfish coup on the landlubbers.

Ridley Hidden camera show.

Kestrel Angry fisherman with a grudge.

Ridley Social experiment.

Kestrel *Alien* jellyfish coup.

Ridley Ah, you're repeating yourself.

Kestrel No, no – they weren't aliens before, that's two different things.

Ridley Two things with the same gist.

Kestrel *[angrily stumbling over words]* Same gist? You said hidden camera show and social ex-priment and those are the same thing, just they air one at the fucking end of it instead of writing it down – that's same gist. You're same gist.

Ridley One is a carefully constructed experiment with scientific—

The toilet flushes, then gurgles as if something is blocked. **Ridley** *and* **Kestrel** *straighten up.*
  Beat.
  They look at one another.

Ridley Well?

Kestrel Well, I'll fetch it. But not cause you said.

Kestrel *crosses over to the toilet –*

Kestrel This had better be the last one though cause your god knows I've places to . . .

– and looks down. She pauses, long enough that **Ridley** *stops to observe.*

Ridley What's wrong?

Kestrel *plunges her hands into the toilet. There is the sound of suction released. She has retrieved a large egg, sizable enough that she has to carry it in both hands. It is almost prehistoric in appearance.*

Ridley Ah.

Kestrel Fucking yeah.

She carries it towards the sink, and rethinks it. She places the egg in the centre of the bathroom floor and stares.

Ridley No.

Kestrel What do you mean no?

Ridley I mean I'm not dealing with that.

Kestrel But – why the fuck not?

Ridley Whatever's going on Kestrel – I mean, whatever, in His
infinite wisdom is going on, we don't understand it.

Beat.

Kestrel You quit 'cause the toilet spat up an egg?

Ridley I don't quit. I just question if this is above our pay grade,
as they say.

Kestrel As fucking who says? It's an egg! It can't even sting like a
jellyfish. We could just sit it here. Wrap it in a towel maybe.

Ridley You're wanting to incubate an egg that came out of the
sewer?

Kestrel I mean, it mighta come out the sea.

Ridley No. No, there's no good that comes from this. I'm telling
you.

*Ridley drops her cleaning supplies and goes to lean against the wall.
Kestrel stays by the egg, perplexed.*

Kestrel You can't just go on general strike here. While you're
ignoring the fucking egg you could at least scrub those tiles.

Ridley I'm stepping back, Kestrel. We don't know what's causing
it.

Kestrel Jesus Christ, mopping the floor isn't what's making the
toilet spew fucking Neptune over here.

Ridley I don't care.

*Kestrel mutters something. She reaches out and prods the egg –
once, twice.*

Kestrel It's really cold. Don't think incubation's much good.
Look, touch it.

Ridley No.

Kestrel But . . . Don't you wonder what it is?

Ridley I do. I wonder what it is. I also wonder what being
electrocuted feels like, I wonder what that's like – but what
I don't do Kestrel, is I don't jam my hand down the plug
socket, Kestrel, because that's a stupid thing to do Kestrel.

Kestrel Pfffft. Could be what's hatching all them jellyfish.

Ridley I don't know how jellyfish are born, I'll admit that
Kestrel. But I somewhat doubt they come from that.

Kestrel . . . well, how come?

Ridley BECAUSE IT LOOKS LIKE A TYRANNOSAUR EGG
YOU FECK

Beat.

Kestrel Alright. Jesus. Language. *[to the egg]* Egg, you're
breaking up a happy home here.

Ridley You can keep cleaning, if you like. But I'm waiting till
[gestures] he comes back and sees what's going on.

Kestrel You'll get fired. I'll get fucking fired via contact high.
We do this, I can go home. Just do the work Ridley, god
knows you've been here long enough.

Ridley God does know.

Kestrel Aw, fuck off with that. You're sitting there watching a
theme park toilet – you watch this toilet whitey up the
Phantom Zone and you're on a god bender?

Ridley Kestrel—

Kestrel Look at that! Look at this thing. Anything could come
out of there.

Ridley You can go ahead and nurse the egg. But I'm not part
of it.

Kestrel Christ, never had to deal with this shite at Asda. You
realise, if you're doing the whole Pontius Pilate thing, his
hands weren't actually washed fucking clean, right?

Ridley I don't care to be lectured on my religion.

Kestrel I'll lecture you on anything I like. I'm young enough to
change – you're a hundred years old and still wiping folks'

    shite off the tiles. Case in point – I have a fucking social life
    to get back to.

Ridley Explain.

Kestrel . . . what do you mean.

Ridley Explain what it is you've to get back in time for. You're
    always going on about your social life, but I've yet to hear
    any actual details. Is it all just the filth on your phone?

Kestrel Naw. Naw there's loads of stuff.

Ridley I'm sure.

Kestrel How the fuck would you know Ridley? How the fuck
    would you know what folk do in their free time? All you
    got to do is tick off the days till that massive coronary
    gets you.

Ridley Well then what do you do in your free time. Explain to
    an old shut-in, *dear.*

Kestrel You are a snide bully, and I hope your heart attack is
    positively fucking atomic.

Ridley Come on, give us a hint.

Kestrel I WATCH NETFLIX WITH A SEVENTY OF VODKA
    UNTIL I PASS OUT

Beat.

Ridley Well I do apologise, that sounds very urgent Kestrel.

Kestrel . . . I hope you get Alzheimer's.

The two of them stand in silence for a moment. **Kestrel** *goes to resume
cleaning, then remembers her words and fetches a towel, wrapping
it around the base of the giant egg. She briefly cups it with her hands.*

Ridley It'll be dead at any rate. What's inside. If it's that cold.

Kestrel You're dead inside.

*The door swings open. They straighten. Trumpet blast. Both of them
point at the egg.*

Ridley & Kestrel Sir, this came up—

Trumpet.

Ridley Well, I think that this calls / for knowledge beyond us,
   sir.

Kestrel I told her not to, I said we should keep / cleaning. I said
   that back in my Asda days—

Ridley I just think that—

Trumpet blast, longer than usual. They are being lectured.

Ridley & Kestrel Yessir.

The door swings shut.

Ridley Look at you, doing as you're told.

Kestrel Awright, calm it. You've done enough. You think being
   enough of a bitch will bring your husband back or
   something?

Ridley Where did you say you saw the boss? Tinder, was it?

Kestrel Ridley—

Ridley I don't think I'm saying anything out of line, dear.
   People get up to all sorts these days. Are you going to
   dispose of that like he said?

Kestrel He said both of us dispose of it Ridley – both-of-us.
   That means you've got to help. Or is that too scary – that
   big egg. Too menacing?

Ridley I'm not saying anything.

Kestrel Good. So we're not fucking talking.

*Kestrel scrubs the floor in silence. Ridley refuses to participate. Every
so often, both shoot glances at the egg, but never at the same time.
Kestrel prods the egg again, but her finger breaks through the shell.*

*Panicking, she tries to cover up the hole with the towel. It slides
down repeatedly, increasingly covered in yellow gunk. Ridley is not
paying attention. Kestrel plugs the hole with a wadded up corner of
the towel. She leans back, examines it, looks around.*

Realising there are no consequences to this, she relaxes.

*Eventually, **Kestrel** rocks back onto her knees and brings out her phone. She plays with it, blank-faced. **Ridley** stares ahead.*

__Kestrel__ plays the Pingu *theme tune from her phone. It gets progressively louder, and louder, until it hits the climax, which is insufferable.*

Ridley I'M JUST WORRIED ABOUT ESCALATION

__Kestrel__ pauses the music.

Kestrel Meaning?

Ridley Hordes of jellyfish, now eggs? What's next? What comes after that? It's escalating, like the Book of – I think we have to be sensible about this. This isn't covered in our contracts.

Kestrel Don't you want to see what comes next? Or if it hatches? That'd be fucking trippy, being born in a space theme park, eh? You'd be like 'is this what the world looks like'—

Ridley We're not covered. We're not covered for any of this, Kestrel. What are we going to do if Mammon himself crawls out of there—

Kestrel You'll have to explain that later—

Ridley Steel claws gripping the bowl! We can go to what's left of the union, but I don't think they'll have procedure for this.

Kestrel Back in my Asda days—

Ridley I DON'T CARE

Beat.

Kestrel Okay. Well, let's say we take a fucking pause. In the eyes of your Nonce Almighty, let's kneel and pray for guidance.

Ridley Well, I don't agree with the tone, but I'm happy with the general outcome.

Kestrel Good. Good. It's fucking compromise. In the face of whatever the shit is going on here.

Ridley Let's hope it makes sense eventually.

Beat.

Ridley Did you break that egg Kestrel?

A PA system rings out. **Ridley** *and* **Kestrel** *look up. The trumpet blasts out over the speakers, in short bursts.*

Kestrel They're closing early?
Ridley Maybe evacuating. Maybe there's jellyfish all over now.
Kestrel Or eggs.
Ridley Or eggs.
Kestrel Should we ask if we're free to go?
Ridley I don't think we'll be included.

The PA system blares angry trumpet. They are not included.

Ridley Well, there's your answer.
Kestrel Could he hear us the whole time?
Ridley . . . it would explain his moods.
Kestrel Goddamnit, I'm never getting home, am I.
Ridley Your poor bottle won't drink itself.
Kestrel . . . you want to split it?
Ridley Yeah alright.

The toilet flushes. They freeze.

The toilet gurgles, blocked. **Ridley** *and* **Kestrel** *look at it.*

The room shakes.

Extremely loud: the call of a humpback whale.

Caoimhin MacNèill / Kevin MacNeil
AN DÈIDH SANTŌKA TANEDA (1882–1940)

tha soilleireachd an t-sneachda
a' lìonadh an taighe
le suaimhneas

ma 's e 's gun reic mi mo bhàrlagan
gus uisge-beatha a cheannach,
am bi an aonaranachd fhathast ann?

bog-fliuch a-rithist an-diugh
tha mi a' coiseachd air slighe
nach aithne dhomh

Paul McQuade
THE WORLD IN OUR HANDS

The door will not open. Padraig tries to crack it: to force the wood to splinter, the hinges to give. Even a little would do, just enough to slip through to work on time, crumpled suit or no. But the door will not open. In the kitchen, Róisín sits on the counter and watches the snow glisten silver in the dark of the early morning.

'Damnú air!' Padraig saves Irish for cursing. 'We're bloody snowed in.'

Róisín eats toast and marmalade and watches the snow fall and wishes she could bring herself to care. But she feels good, buried in all this white.

A robin hops along the eye-high snow, leaving tracks in the surface of the drift. Róisín finishes her toast and licks a glob of grapefruit marmalade from her finger. The last of the batch she had made last summer, when things were going better. It is harder to care in winter, she thinks, as though the cold numbs more than fingers and noses and ears. Padraig walks into the kitchen to see why she hasn't replied.

'Did you hear me?' he asks. 'We're snowed in.'

She looks and, for a moment, barely recognises the man in front of her, this man with whom she has made love and grapefruit jam, a home for three years. This man with whom she had made a baby, almost.

His dark curls are still wet from his shower; drops cling to his short beard. For a moment, she wonders if the baby would have looked like him.

'Oh,' she says. What does he want her to say?

'It's all right for you,' he says. 'You don't need to get to work.'

She looks at him. The snow has made her serene. She is mindless, and for the first time in a long time, without pain.

'I'm sorry,' he says. He lifts his arm a fraction then lets it fall. He is still unsure. As though he wants to touch her but feels she might shatter at even the slightest embrace. Maybe she would.

She makes no move towards him. She is concerned that if she moves she will lose the calm the snow has brought her. She opens up the empty jar of marmalade and cleans the sides with a finger. Outside, a robin walks the eye-high snow.

Padraig phones work and tells them he can't come in. As she washes out the empty jam jar, it seems as though the conversation is taking longer than it should. The water is near scalding, her fingers red as she sets the clean glass upside down on the counter to dry. When she turns around, Padraig has his head in his hands and his eyes closed.

'They told me not to bother coming in again,' he says. 'Gerry said I've already taken too much time off.' The snow has taken her thoughts. She moves to him without thinking, without reticence, and holds his head to her stomach.

'What are we going to do?' he asks. The words tremble in her abdomen. It is the most they have touched in the weeks since. Out of the corner of her eye, she sees the snow drift down, flake by flake. She shivers.

'Snow,' she says, but the words stick. She clears her throat and brings his face to hers. Tears glisten in his eyes. She cannot remember the last time she felt this way, or when he last smiled like that. For a brief moment, it is as though nothing has happened.

'I've got an idea,' she says.

As they pull the duvet off the bed and move it to the sofa, she remembers dragging her own to the couch as a child on Saturday mornings to watch cartoons. There is something of the same excitement; unbridled, unformed, as she watches Padraig shed his suit and put on pyjama bottoms and an old t-shirt, pale red fabric loose on his collarbones. She is still in her housecoat when she gets under the covers with him and turns on the television. Their limbs overlap carelessly. On the screen, a woman tells them about snow: feet of it falling in Connemara, cars capsized on roadsides, window wipers still trying to beat back the great white hush that is slowly covering all of Ireland.

First the news, then a talk show about paternity tests. They both laugh when some jilted party comes on stage screaming, but there is an edge to the laughter, as if they are close to something dangerous. It is Padraig who changes the channel, searching for a movie. Morning melts into afternoon. Jimmy Stewart peers into a window from the safety of his wheelchair. They sit wrapped in each other, comfortable. Róisín wonders if this comfort is the same as the one that was there before, or if this is something new, some deeper sense of ease that comes only to those who survive. Has she survived? Jimmy Stewart holds his broken leg and groans. When it heals, she tells herself, the break will become the strongest part of the bone.

'You hungry?' Padraig whispers, as though even the tremor of his vocal cords would be enough to upset the calm.

'Starving.' It is only as she says it that she realises how true it is. Old muscles ache, old appetites loosen, as if her body is beginning to speak to her once more. Her belly gnaws and churns. The broken part becomes the strongest place, she tells herself. Beyond the window, the snow continues to fall.

'Let's make lunch,' he says. She is surprised; he is not one to cook. He lifts her by the hand from the couch and she feels herself buoyant, weightless, taken by an unexpected joy. As she cuts onions and he sets water to boil, she feels that same excitement, the cartoon morning one, the anything-might-happen one.

'Where's the pasta?' he asks.

'I think there's some left in the top cupboard,' she says.

A small, flat crunch. The door handle is still in his hand but Padraig's eyes are fixed on what has fallen out. Stag and cat and dinosaur press their faces against a veil of clear plastic. All those little toys he had bought in the excitement, when her blood test came back, forgotten in the cupboard where she had thrown them for fear of bad luck.

'You can't buy things for the baby until it's born,' she had said. 'You'll jinx it, Padraig. Besides, you can't give a newborn things like that to play with.'

'Don't be daft,' he told her. 'It was only a euro. I was excited.'

She stares at the bag: is this what had caused it, this bag of lifeless animals? No, she tells herself, though a part of her wishes she could put it all on him, on this bag that lies there, reminding them of what they have lost.

Silence. They are both afraid to speak. A robin glances by on the eye-high snow. The jam jar on the kitchen counter is streaked where the water has dried.

'Don't,' she says as he stoops down to snatch the bag up. She keeps the knife in her hand, looks at the snow, and moves, sedately, to collect the bag herself. He eyes the knife as she puts the bag down and jumps when she cuts it open. Dogs and bears and crocodiles spill over the kitchen table. An iguana tumbles into the black and white linoleum and is lost.

'What're you doing?' he asks. He hears the fright in his voice as he realises how distant her thoughts are from his, how much remains hidden. He tries to drag his eyes from the knife and, unsure what to do, simply watches as she gathers the jam jar, the one that had housed marmalade from last summer, when they had lain on the grass in the garden and drank gin cocktails, when they made love in the long orange sunsets. When they had made a baby, almost.

He watches as she takes a tube of superglue from the drawer under the sink and fixes a plastic doe to the lid of the jar. She stops for a moment, as if looking for something, then takes one of the Christmas cards down from the windowsill and scrapes at the front with the knife. The blade still gleams with juice from the onion. She takes the jar to the sink and fills it with water, closes the lid, seals it shut, and hands it to him. The jar weighs more than he thought; he almost struggles to right it. Silver glitter dances in the water, cascades down on the flank of the doe. Without thinking, he steps forward and kisses her.

It is not their usual kiss. He simply presses his lips to hers, applies a little pressure, and she presses back. She is unsure what to think. There is nothing that might be called passion in it, but something else, something that makes her feel naked. He kisses her. She returns it. All of this in what seems like one moment, stretching out as far as the snowfields outside. When they stop, he puts his lips on the forehead and whispers, 'I'm so sorry.'

'I know,' she says. And it passes: the moment, the rest, whatever has been in the air these past weeks. Not gone but simply lessened.

She gathers the rest of the old jam jars from the cupboard and they sit at the kitchen table gluing animals to the lids and scraping glitter off the Christmas cards. Eight snowglobes they make, and for each, Róisín or Padraig invents a story, about the life it leads, in its glass jar, how the dog has a gambling addiction, and the hedgehog is frustrated by how loud its neighbours are at night, nocturnal as it is. It feels good to laugh, to put their minds somewhere else. For a moment, at least.

The rest of the animals they scatter around the house: a stag in front of the bathroom mirror, a cat on the bedroom windowsill, a racoon by the photograph they keep next to the key dish in the hall. Arm in arm in front of Neuschwanstein Castle, two winters prior, the ramparts snow-covered, looking more like an iced cake than anything real. The two in the picture seem like strangers to her. The broken part becomes the strongest, she tells herself, as she places the toy next to the photo frame and returns to the kitchen.

Once the pasta is finished, they eat surrounded by animals. Now and again she puts her fork down to shake a jar and watch the animal inside lose itself, only to re-emerge a few seconds later. She envies it its steady place in a world that continues to spin. Padraig watches her, unsure, but amused. After lunch they return to the safety of the sofa.

When the cold lessens and the blizzard breaks, Róisín tells Padraig she's going to the bathroom and sneaks to the front door on the way. It opens with a shudder. Cold air rushes in, as though the world had been holding its breath the entire time. In the dishwater light, the snow goes on for miles: houses obliterated, white on white. No homes in sight. The world outside seems so vast to her, as if neither of them could ever hope to fill it. But, she reminds herself, she is capable of making things, no matter how small. Like love and grapefruit jam. Or a baby. Almost.

Callum McSorley
THE LAST GOOD THING

When they changed the Irn-Bru recipe, Mark managed to buy a pallet of the old stuff on eBay which had fallen off a lorry. Literally. The cans were bashed to fuck inside the plastic wrap, the arse falling out the bottom of the box.

> *. . . speedboat, submarine, yacht, life preservers, paddle board, desert island, getaway, coconuts filled with rum, straws, pineapple slices, dancing women in grass skirts . . .*

Three couldn't be salvaged, crushed and empty of their sticky orange contents which now covered the remaining cans, and many more had to be opened with a knife and drained into a glass before drinking (not the optimal way to enjoy it) but the rest Mark drank one by one, spacing them out over the years until there was just one left – the last proper can of Bru in the known world.

> *. . . Mustang, empty road, American blacktop, high-speed chase, make this baby fly . . .*

He was saving it for a special occasion and then he got made redundant. The can became The Last Good Thing in Life so he decided to have it.

As soon as he yanked the ring-pull he knew something was different. Irn-Bru opens with the kind of hiss that makes you sneeze as if a dandelion's been stuffed right up your beak. It sparkles like caesium in water. It has a boiling fizz you could clean diamonds with. This one did not.

> *. . . palatial, turrets, crenels, chandeliers, fridge, wine cellar, hangover immunity . . .*

Mark put his eye to the opening and an eye looked back.

Fuck! He dropped it. The can hit the floor and launched across the kitchen tiles, propelled by its contents hosing out like tear gas from a canister, a whirl of colours as it tornadoed itself upright and formed into a shape.

$330 billion – cost of ending world hunger by 2030.

Mark stared at a gaseous mirror image of himself. When it moved, an echoing image-trace followed it, like the first visual stages of acid kicking in. Mark checked his own hands, his own movements, but they were singular and solid.

It spoke with his voice. As many wishes as ye like, it said, as many as ye can think ae, as long as ye keep makin them.

As many as I like?

. . . lobster roll, claw meat, salt, lemon, steak cooked on a barbecue by Guy Fieri, frosted tips, undo . . .

Unlimitet. Forever. As long as ye don't stop wishin.

Isn't it usually just three?

Ye done this before? I says as many as ye want, whatever yer heart desires.

So if I wanted . . .

A cheeseburger appeared in his hand. The kind of burger you see on the pictures at McDonald's rather than the kind of ones they actually serve. Mark started to eat, the meat exquisitely moist and charred, the bun sweet, the pickles bursting with sharp vinegar. But before he'd gotten a few bites deep, it was gone. And he was still hungry.

. . . New York, LA, Tokyo, Seoul, Bangkok, Venice, Milan, Paris, Cancun, the very top of Mount Everest, the bottom of the Mariana Trench . . .

I telt ye, ye need tae keep on wishin.

He tried again but no cheeseburger appeared in his hand.

> *$11.4 trillion – collective wealth of the world's billionaires,*
> *which grew by 20% in 2020.*

One mare thing: ye cannae wish for the same thing twice.

Being sly, he wished for a Whopper this time, and he got a Whopper, and as he ate it, he also wished for chips, which duly appeared, and then tomato ketchup and a milkshake, and onion rings, and mozzarella dippers and BBQ dipping sauce and napkins and when he got halfway through, it all disappeared because he couldn't think of anything else to wish for, which was fine because he was full.

> *. . . Armani suit, pinstripes, '50s gangster hat, silk tie, platinum*
> *tie pin, tommy gun, shiny shoes, comfy shoes, Jordans,*
> *jump high enough to dunk . . .*

Wit if I wish tae be a millionaire?

> *. . . Mera Peak, vintage Adidas, Beatles reunion . . .*

Then ye'll be one as long as ye keep makin mare wishes. Seems pointless tae me though, why spend when ye can just wish? It's your go, but, dae what ye want. I'm just here tae make yer dreams come true, not gie ye life advice.

> *. . . like Heidi Klum, Kate Moss, Kylie, Angelina,*
> *Audrey Tautou, Megan Fox, Jackie Bird . . .*

*

RECAP – THE RULES:

Mark can wish for anythin he wants, no exceptions. He can wish for love, bring back the deid, take Partick Thistle tae the top ae the Champion's League. Anythin.

Mark has unlimitet wishes tae make.

However, the results ae the wish only remain **as long as he continues tae make mare wishes**.

> . . . *Clooney, Driver, Sinatra, Bogart, Willis pre-bald,*
> *Schwarzenegger, Brad Pitt's face, The Rock's body,*
> *hung like Rocco Sifreddi . . .*

Failure tae make a new wish will cause previous wishes tae cease tae exist. (e.g. The first time he had sex wae a wummin he'd wished out ae thin air, Mark lay in post-orgasmic bliss for five minutes and shook himself awake tae find the wummin gone, along with his NY-style penthouse, his Rolls Royce Phantom, and even his silky boxer shorts wae foot-long chopper inside. He asked for a baker's dozen ae inches next time [within the rules, see below].)

Mark CANNOT make the same wish twice.

Variables on the same wish are acceptet as long as they are not identical. I will be the arbitrator on what is or isnae acceptable, i.e. whether the pish is bein taken.

> *$774 – average annual salary in Rwanda.*

*

He wished for a new house, on the spot exactly where his rented bedroom in Partick was right now. He wished it had three floors, he wished it had a basement with a cinema and a bar, he wished it had a heated swimming pool under a glass roof. He wished it had columns along the front, and a circular driveway with a fountain in the middle, and a vast garden which pushed back all his neighbours' houses, who adapted as if nothing had changed, as if things had always been this way, that they had always been camped either side of MTV Cribs and its vast grounds on White Street. (He used a wish to clean up all the dug shite in the neighbourhood, for which people didn't even know to be grateful because now it had always been so that there was no shite on White. Its alternative name had never now been uttered or even crossed anyone's mind.)

> *. . . play the piano, paint a masterpiece, top-flight footballer, write the Great Scottish Novel, skin diver, marathon-stamina lover, fly like a bird, fly like Superman, X-ray vision, read people's minds, undo, be tall enough to step across the Grand Canyon . . .*

He wished himself handsome, with a chest you'd be proud to wax. The genie stayed the same: bags under the eyes, hair receding, teeth just a little crooked, a little yellow, just regular old Mark in smoky ghost-form, legs twisting together into a tail whose tip ended in the can of Bru. Fae humble origins, it said with a wink.

> *$281 trillion – global debt total.*

He wished for a tennis court and people to play tennis with and a guy to hand out drinks and towels and fetch balls that went astray – though he then started to just wish for more balls, unlimited balls. He thrashed Andy Murray then they had a few drinks after. He wished health and happiness for the man and his future as the second-best Scottish tennis player of all time. The genie got right up in Murray's grill. Smile, son, it said. The tennis pro looked right through it.

> *. . . be a dog, be a rabbit, be a bear, be a dinosaur, bring back the dinosaurs, bring back the meteor . . .*

He wished for a new motor and as he drove down the street in his Lambo it morphed as it went, all sorts of bits and pieces changing, the engine growling and growing, the tyre profiles shifting, paint bleeding quicksilver to metallic red. Micro changes. Micro wishes.

That was a good way to do it, to keep it all ticking over. Keep wishing, keep wishing, and nothing fades. So what if you can't concentrate on the road? One wish and the traffic moves aside for you. One wish and all bones are healed, skulls taped up. One wish and the car flies over everything, the view almost enough to make Mark pause and lose his breath, make his flying car disappear into a puff of cloud. Mind tae wish fir a parachute. The genie rode shotgun, did his best and failed not to say anything sarky. He didn't hide judgement as he watched Mark scrape and scrabble for more and more all the time, constantly trying to think of the next thing while simultaneously trying to enjoy the last thing and forgetting all the things before it which he was desperate not to lose. Once, to keep clawing himself forwards, he wished a snail safe passage across a road – the genie called him a Charitable Fucker and Mark told the genie to get back in its can, which it duly did, although the request wasn't a wish.

. . . healthy, happy, well fed, well liked, successful, fulfilled . . .

He wished for a private jet, champagne in a bucket, pornography-inspired stewardesses to sook his cap as he flew to wherever – the moon, if he wanted. And he realised he didn't even have to travel, he could just wish himself there – *zap!* – and he could still get his cap sooked anywhere. Sometimes the genie stayed and watched, making Mark uncomfortable – though he started to get used to its ghostly non-presence and became adept at ignoring it – other times it boiled back down into the Irn-Bru can, a wry smile on its sulky, punching bag face. Old Mark's face.

1 in 10 – people who don't have access to clean water close to home.

He stood on the surface of the moon, no spacesuit, breathing in nothing comfortably, being very careful to continue to make wishes – a constant murmur bubbling inside his brain, never quiet, even two hundred and thirty-nine thousand miles from the nearest human being on this silver, desolate, beautiful ball of rock, watching the Earth spin silently over the horizon. He wished for a football to kick, a set of golf clubs and a ball – and then some more balls – a dune buggy to drive around in the moon dust, a dog to take a floaty walk with.

He wished for a wife. He wished she looked like Marylin Monroe, then he wished she looked like Eva Mendez, then Natalie Portman, and on and on, the woman a shapeshifter. He wished she loved him and understood him. He wished for a cook and a cleaner because he didn't want her doing those things. He wished she understood his need to continue to fuck other people he conjured up. So she did.

> The top 1% of the world's wealthiest people collectively own 43% of all personal wealth.

He wished for kids then wished he hadn't. Just kidding. He wished they adored him, and liked the things he liked, and that they were beautiful and smart and never got themselves into trouble. They were babies then quickly toddlers then kids, skipped the teens. He made wishes for them: toys, friends, hobbies, skills, talents.

Times were good when he had plenty of things to wish for. But the moments when his brain was lean and running dry were filled with drowning terror, and the more he accrued, the worse the fear of losing it all got, even if he never played with his fighter jet anymore, or left his personal trainer – 1960s Muhammad Ali – shadow-boxing in the gym alone. There was no time for any of it. Only the next wish, the genie's smirk as it granted it. Very imaginative, it would say. Classy, pal. Just wit the world needs mair ae, son. Aye, that's the answer tae wit dae ye get the man who's got everythin. All in Mark's voice – though Mark had never

consciously worn a look so withering. But he could bear it –
for whatever he wanted, whatever he dreamed of or desired, for
whatever whim popped into his feverish, churning mind to be
made real just as quickly, he could bear the scorn of the genie or
of the entire world for that matter. Fuck em all. He wished to be
immune from criticism and – *zap!* – he was.

The bottom 50% own 1% of all personal wealth.

He made wishes for his own friends also – he wished them millions,
wished them happiness and good times, wished them away on
holidays with him to drink and do fucked-up shit then wish it all
away if he had to. Mark couldn't quite remember which of his
friends were real – in the *real* sense – and which he'd made for
himself on his new plane of reality. Did it matter? Only if he slipped
or slowed down. His hands were always clammy with panic sweat,
his heart hard and swollen into a ball of steroidal muscle pumping
out gruel-like sustenance at a choppy one hundred BPM.

Because he could never forget that his world was made of
kinetic sand. Viscoelastic existence. Solid, compact, real – as long
as he kept applying pressure, kept moving it, playing with it, like
walking across a swimming pool filled with custard. Wish, wish,
wish. More, more, more. Piling it all up. The second he stopped,
the second he forgot, it would all start to crumble to dust. The
house would moulder, its bricks cracking, walls drunkenly leaning
inwards, whispering away at the edges. The pool would dry. The
cars would be up on blocks, metal corroding. And the people.
Who would be left?

*. . . jump from the top of the Burj Khalifa AND LIVE, touch the
surface of the sun, create aliens on other planets
to commune with, invade, destroy, repair,
make love to, remove, renege, reassess . . .*

Just Mark alone in his kitchen with a can of original recipe Irn-Bru. The last in the known world. But it had a genie inside it, and he could start all over again as long as he could think of anything else he wanted.

> *. . . a night on the Titanic, a seat at the Last Supper, take a*
> *bucket of popcorn to Ford's Theatre . . .*

Andrea Mejía
THE PRETTIEST GIRL IN TOWN

The first time my husband and I visit you at the home, you tell us the story of the day you earned the title of 'Miss Navidad' in your pueblo's Christmas fair. You say it was 'meant to be' because your name is Natividad Mendoza, and you were born on Christmas Day, 1938. You also say you were one of the prettiest girls in town.

The only problem was you were too skinny, and back then beauty queens in your pueblo were curvy, with wide hips and butts, round faces, and plump red lips. People said you were pretty for a skinny girl. And yet, you signed up for the pageant to show how lovely you were. You were eighteen years old, almost nineteen, and your sisters teased you and said you'd lose to Lupe Castañeda, a beautiful girl with a sweet voice who also happened to be Father Macedonio's goddaughter. They said you had to *try* to look prettier if you wanted to win. So, they did your hair in a bun with lots of hairspray and you wore a beautiful lilac dress that matched your brown eyes.

When the pageant came on Christmas Eve, after Father Macedonio's prayer, you showed them your best feature. It wasn't your dress or your body, or your eyes or hairdo, but the smile you now flash at my husband and me. You say you smiled and waved to the audience, and everyone fell in love with you, including the judges, and so you became 'Miss Navidad, 1957'. You say happiness makes you pretty, but love makes you prettier, and before we leave, you ask us to keep love and smiles in our marriage because together they make it beautiful.

On our second visit, you ask us if you've told us the story of the day you were named 'Miss Navidad'. You already did, and yet you retell it. Now you say the pageant girls were ugly and had ugly names as well. None were like you, Natividad Mendoza, born on Christmas Day, 1938. You say the other girls were skinny too, whereas Lupe Castañeda had an hourglass shape. Men in town

were crazy for her. All men, except your then-boyfriend, Artemio
Luján. You met him when he rode across your father's rancho. You
had to hide him from your father; otherwise he'd think Artemio
was a trespasser and shoot him.

You say the Miss Navidad pageant was a 'rite of passage', so girls
signed up at least once in their lifetime. You were never interested,
but you heard this year's prize was a mare, and you wanted her to
ride with Artemio, your handsome charro. Even though you won,
you two never rode together because a stray bullet took him away
from you on New Year's Eve. You hadn't met grandfather then. You
say you didn't love him as you loved Artemio, but he was a decent
man. The love of your life was Artemio, and to him, you were the
prettiest girl in town.

You took the crown home because you were a cheerful girl,
and you smile at us the way you did back when you paraded
before the judges and the town at the Christmas fair. You miscal-
culate the year, though, because you say it was in 1956, but that's
okay. Sometimes I mix up the dates and years, and you've had a
long life, and we still hope you'll live longer than the time the
doctors gave you. We leave the home and promise to be back in a
fortnight. You say goodbye and wave like a queen, the way you did
when you became Miss Navidad.

The third time we visit you, we find you lying on your bed, closer
to the window. You smile at us and introduce yourself: Natividad
Mendoza, born on Christmas Day, you can't remember the year.
You ask for Grandfather. I tell you he passed away when I was a
kid, about twenty years ago. You nod. Of course, how could you
forget it? The day he died was the anniversary of your happiest day,
the day you were named the prettiest girl in town. Grandfather
died in spring, but I say nothing. You tell the story again, and you
mention your sisters and your hairdo, but the dress you wore has
no colours, and you can't remember the prize.

You say you were too skinny, but despite that, your then-boyfriend
Artemio Luján loved you. He desired you so much he tried to steal

you and take you to the mountains. However, the day he trespassed your rancho and kidnapped you, he regretted his choice because he saw you cry. He loved you for your pretty smile, and he didn't want to take that away. He told you your smile was your loveliest feature, so you showed it off at the pageant. You frown and bite your lips trying to remember the year and how old you were, but then laugh off your deceitful memory, and I laugh with you while tears fall down my face, and you laugh even louder thinking you're a good comedian. Before we leave, I promise you I'll be back next week. But you tell me to never promise that, because Artemio did so the last time you saw him, and a few hours later somebody shot him during a bar fight.

The following week, you're at the same spot by the window. You see me and call me the name of your elder sister. I sit by your side and braid your grey hair, and you tell me that was the hairdo you wore when you earned the title of Miss Navidad when you were young. You ask me if I'm going to take part in the pageant next week. I say I don't know. Our family hasn't been in your hometown in decades, but I omit that piece of information; I don't want Time to be a killjoy. You say there was a curvy girl with a beautiful voice in the contest and she was about to take the crown home, but your boyfriend Artemio wouldn't have it, so he climbed up on stage and snatched the crown from the judges and put it on your head because you were, to him, the prettiest girl in town. And you laughed because Artemio would only bring smiles and kisses to your lips before bringing tears to your eyes on your birthday, when you found out a bullet took his life. It was Christmas Day, 1950 . . . something.

His funeral mass took place on New Year's Eve because everyone was busy with festivities, and no one wanted to say farewell to a rascal like Artemio Luján. You can't remember the colours you wore during the pageant, but you say in your colourful wardrobe we can find the black dress you wore for his funeral. You cried your sorrows at your pueblo's church, but by his grave you smiled and thanked him for giving you a crown and calling you the prettiest girl in town. Before we leave, you ask me when your birthday is. I say Christmas is in a month. Right, you almost forget it. You're Natividad, and you were born on Christmas Day, *Navidad*. You nod and smile because that's what pretty girls do when they say goodbye.

In the visit before your birthday, you don't move from your bed and ask our names. You say you're Natividad Mendoza, bastard daughter of Emiliano Zapata, even though he died almost twenty years before you were born. You tell me you're 'Miss Navidad', the prettiest girl of your pueblo, and ask for Artemio Luján, because you want to show off the mare you won. The last time you saw him, he told you he'd celebrate your victory with his friends and a few tequilas at the cantina, but you just want to flee with him. He can get high-spirited when he drinks too much. You don't want to look worried because Artemio says you're pretty all the time, but especially when you're happy. You ask me to put you in the wedding dress in your wardrobe, but there's none. You're longing to join your brave, gallant charro forever, the man who loves you dearly and only brings smiles to your lips.

Our last visit is not at the home but at the hospital. At some point the disease catches up, and you forget how to tell a story. You can't remember my name and yours. I find you sleeping, wired to an oxygen machine that barely keeps you in our side of Life. Your eyes flutter as you wake up, and you ask who I am. I say I am Artemia, your granddaughter, named after my mother. You blink and nod, and with a soft laugh ask, 'Who am I?' I clutch your hand, as if that could keep you longer with us. You're Natividad Mendoza, born on Christmas Day 1938. You were named 'Miss Navidad' when you were eighteen years old, and whatever reason made you smile – a healthy mare, proving your sisters and your town wrong, the hopes of love, or longing to elope with your handsome charro – you were and still are the prettiest girl in town.

Claire O'Connor
NIGHT SWIMMING WITH GODZILLA

From inside, you wouldn't know the El Paso Bar is five blocks from the beach. It's got warped walls and dark carpet, and the sole window faces a sign for the I-5. Every fifteen minutes, if no one puts in any coins, the jukebox automatically plays a random mariachi song.

We open at ten a.m., and it usually doesn't take long to get the first customer of the day. Today it's Godzilla. He's not as tall as you would think: maybe nine feet, ten tops. He stoops through the doorway and drags that thick tail of his across the floor.

He doesn't fit on a stool, so he sits on a crate next to the bar and asks for a pitcher. We only have Bud Lite on draft, so that's what I pour. I restock bottles of Pacifico and Modelo and try not to stare, but when I wipe down the bar, I sneak glances at the webbing between his fingers and the armour of scales on the backs of his hands.

'I'm a big fan,' I say.

He shrugs. He sighs. I hold my breath. But he never breathes fire, or radiation, or whatever it is that burns inside of him. When Sandra, a regular, comes in, she gives Godzilla the once over and sits a few barstools down.

'White zinfandel,' she says with a wink. She clears her throat. Godzilla looks up, and she flashes a smile. She's missing a tooth, not her front tooth, but one tooth over from that. I feel bad pulling out the jug of pink wine. Nothing good comes in a jug like this. Sandra moves one barstool closer to Godzilla.

'Where are you from, stranger?'

Godzilla doesn't look up from his pitcher. 'Monster Island.'

'Ooh. An island. That sounds nice.'

Godzilla shakes his head. There's a scar on his face from his eyebrow to his ear. You don't see that in the movies. 'There are no beaches. Only rocks.'

Sandra shrugs. 'I don't like the feeling of sand on my feet.'

Horns blare. The jukebox always makes me jump. The music relaxes into a strumming of guitars. No matter how many mariachi songs I hear, they all sound the same: happy and sad at the same time.

Sandra stands and sidles up to Godzilla. 'You wanna dance?'

Godzilla stiffens. 'I can't dance.'

'It's not rocket science.' She runs her finger along the jagged plates of his spine.

'No.' The muscles of his jaw clench. His bony plates stand erect. 'Sometimes I don't know my own strength.'

Sandra slumps back into her stool. She sips her wine and says she has a job interview at one o'clock: telemarketing. I look at the clock. It's almost noon.

'Do you like it there?' I ask Godzilla. 'On Monster Island?' I picture the other monsters, enormous lizards and gigantic insects, multi-headed monsters roaring, multi-legged monsters stomping through the dense undergrowth, unclassifiable monsters slipping into dripping tunnels and caves or soaring overhead, flapping enormous leathery wings.

Godzilla frowns. 'It's like an Indian reservation, minus the casinos.' He drinks straight from the pitcher. 'What about you?' He wipes foam from his leathery lips. 'Do you like it here?'

I shrug. Six months earlier my mom almost died – insulin pump malfunction. That's why I came home. That's what I told myself when I left the big city along with a series of dead-end jobs and a girl who didn't love me back.

My mom recovered quickly. She bought a bicycle and enough pairs of spandex shorts to clothe the Tour de France. I paid two hundred bucks for a week-long bartending course then dropped off a resume at every bar in a thirty mile radius, even the cowboy-themed lounge where they made the women wear booty shorts and chaps. The manager took my application and looked me up and down. I was wearing baggy jeans, and my hair was cut

short like a boy's. He didn't call. None of the bars called except
the El Paso Bar.

*

When Cherry comes in, she doesn't notice Godzilla, just orders
a Dos Equis and takes it straight to the back behind the pool
table. No baby carriage, like the owner warned, but when Cherry
starts looking over her shoulder, I know it's coming. Soon she's
talking to the empty space next to the pool table, and when she
starts to scream bloody murder, I yell, 'Cherry!' She looks up,
her eyes wide. 'It's okay, there's no one there.'

She nods and takes a sip of her beer and then covers it with her
cocktail napkin. Godzilla looks at Cherry, then turns back to his
beer. 'Everyone is afraid of things that aren't there,' he says.

'You don't seem afraid of much,' I say.

Godzilla hiccups. It sounds like a tiny version of his iconic roar.

I wonder how long it took him to get here from Monster Island.
I look for gills – he must breathe underwater – but the skin on his
neck is gnarled, ropy, and his and throat, while thick, is smooth
and seamless.

Sandra orders her third wine. It's a quarter to one.

'Is your interview in person, or is it by phone?' I ask.

She shrugs. 'I'm going to get my hairdressing licence back.' She
holds out her hand for the wine. 'It was all a big misunderstanding.'
She takes a drink. 'Do you ever get the feeling that nobody understands you?'

I nod. I refused to go cycling with my mom, but she wore me
down until I went stand up paddle boarding. Every muscle in my
body tensed as we made our way along a lagoon, or an estuary – I
wasn't sure what to call the brackish water that snaked through
clumps of brown grass and festering algae.

'You know, there weren't a lot of options for women in my
day. Nurse, teacher, secretary.' My mom took long, even strokes.
She was a nurse. 'Don't get me wrong. I like helping people. But

women can do anything these days. You can do whatever makes you happy.'

*

Eduardo comes into the El Paso Bar a little before two with a spring in his step. He pays Sandra's tab and puts some coins in the jukebox. A man's voice trills with yearning, and the two of them dance, pressed against each other in a way that makes me blush.

Godzilla hasn't moved. I think of a volcano, dormant. 'How long are you in town?' I ask.

'Just the day.'

Cherry leaves, walks right out the door. A few minutes later she returns, removes the cocktail napkin from her beer bottle, takes a sip, then replaces the napkin. She leaves again.

I google Godzilla. Someone compares him to a Shinto god of destruction, incapable of being measured by human notions of good and evil. Destruction brings rebirth, paving the way for something new.

Eduardo puts more money in the jukebox, and an uptempo song fills the space. Sandra shrieks with laughter as they twirl around. Every time she laughs, Godzilla winces. His skin is the colour and texture of obsidian.

'Can I ask you something?'

Godzilla sighs, but he nods.

I want to ask if he's glad we created him with our overflow of toxic waste, or if he resents us for making something that never should have existed? Deep down, does he want to destroy us or save us? Does he ever get confused between the two?

But I don't.

'How do you breathe underwater?'

Godzilla bares his teeth, huge and glistening. I think he's smiling. 'I don't breathe at all.' He squints. 'What is it like, to breathe?'

'It's overrated.'

I didn't tell Godzilla about the yoga class I tried. With each breath I felt something inside me fly away. We arranged ourselves into uncomfortable positions, and then we lay on the floor and pretended to be dead.

Afterwards I ate dinner with my parents on the couch as we all watched the evening news unravel its ticker-tape of disasters. My mom had made an apple pie. She let me serve myself, but she brought my dad's share. She was trying to get him to eat healthier by serving him gradually smaller and smaller pieces of pie.

'You can talk to us, you know,' my mom said. My dad went to the kitchen to retrieve the canister of whipped cream. My mom lowered her voice. 'Are you gay? Are you bi?'

I poked at my piece of pie. I'm the only one in the family who doesn't love apple pie.

'Are you trans? Are you nonbinary?'

'Don't put me in a box!' I hissed.

When my dad returned, he looked at his tiny piece of pie and doused the plate with a flurry of whipped cream.

*

The lone window in the El Paso Bar rattles, and I steel myself for an earthquake. But we're next to the Marine base, and the trembling is just the reverberation of sanctioned missiles plying the earth, rehearsing for foreign lands. When the two homeless vets, one pushing the other's wheelchair, come in and put their day's pile of change on the bar, I count out the nickels and dimes while they gape at Godzilla. They have the exact amount for a pitcher. I hand them two glasses.

Godzilla twitches. When he turns, glaring, the one in the wheelchair says, 'Thank you for your service.'

Godzilla's face softens. 'You, too, buddy.'

The first time Godzilla emerged from the ocean, he wreaked havoc on Tokyo. But after that, for the most part, he saved humankind from other, deadlier threats.

The homeless vets are the only ones who ever tip me. Sometimes customers try to buy me drinks, but I always decline. *I have to drive home.* They shake their heads, bewildered. The homeless vets don't have money to spare for a tip but they give me things they find on the street. My favourite is a sherbet-coloured knit hat that I took home and washed. When I sent a picture of myself wearing the hat to the girl, she texted, *Cute!* For days I wondered, did she mean the hat or me?

While Godzilla and the vets swap war stories, the bar fills up. It's after five. Men and women shout in Spanish and sing along to the mariachi music. A group of men play pool while a group of women taunt them. I'm supposed to work until six, but the owner calls and says Maricela is running late, can I work until eight? No problema, I say, eyeing Godzilla as he leans closer to the vets, straining to hear them above the roar of the bar. They talk about duty and purpose, peace and possibility.

My best gig in the city had been working at an art museum. A foot in the door, I told myself, but I worked in the gift shop. I had a degree in art history, along with half the museum guards. All the curators and creatives worked on the top floor, closed to the public. In addition to selling postcards, I spent most of my day directing visitors to the nearest bathroom.

When the museum hosted a special exhibit on Gauguin, the gift shop sold flowery scarves and candles in miniature coconut husks, and the kids' corner sported an assortment of tropical stuffed animals. My favourite was the large plush dolphin. When you unzipped its belly, a hodgepodge of smaller sea animals tumbled out: a turtle, a shark, a squid, a starfish. When I told the girl, expecting her to laugh, she said: *There are infinite possible lives inside of us.*

*

A young guy, clean-cut, and his manicured date enter the bar. Pressed shirt, aftershave – off-duty Marine. Compared to the rest of the clientele, the pair of them look like polished jewels. They order appletinis from the happy hour menu. They are the first people ever to order a cocktail here. The El Paso Bar only has a beer and wine license, so for mixed drinks the owner uses soju, a Korean potato liqueur that's only twenty per cent alcohol. I explain what the drinks are made from, and they say they'll have them anyway.

The couple speak in the polite tones of a first date. As I prepare the fluorescent green elixir, I wonder if they'll have a second date. I wonder if at their wedding they'll toast flutes of champagne and reminisce about their knock-off appletini in a Mexican bar five blocks from the sea. Sandra and Eduardo are nowhere to be seen, and I hope, wherever they've gone, they will be kind to each other. I hope Cherry finds someone who will help keep her phantoms at bay.

Godzilla clacks his pitcher with a claw. 'One more.'

I refill his pitcher. 'It must be tough to be the King of the Monsters. Sounds like a lot of responsibility.'

Godzilla's brow is always furrowed, but he frowns even harder.

'I'm not a king. That's a bad English translation. In Japanese, I don't even have a gender.'

'No gender?'

He looks me up and down. 'I'm an *it*. My original name, Gojira, is a mixture of two words, gorilla and whale.' He sighs. 'They're majestic animals – whales – don't you think?'

I nod. 'I love their songs. What do you think of gorillas?'

He drinks. 'King Kong. It's complicated.'

One of my favourite artists, Walton Ford, painted three enormous close-up portraits of King Kong. In one the ape looks angry, in another, scared, and in the last, forlorn.

Complicated. I nod. One night the girl from the city drunk-dialled me. *I miss you,* she purred. She had left the city, too, and retreated to her hometown. But her hometown was hip: Austin, TX. The day after she called me she posted a photo on Instagram of her and a boy with a handlebar moustache. I wanted to eviscerate him with radioactive breath. I wanted to singe his facial hair before melting his skin and bones.

According to Google Maps, the largest city halfway between Austin and my hometown in nowhere, California is El Paso, Texas. El Paso is a border town, sprawling across countries, blurring into Juarez, Mexico. My Spanish is limited. According to the internet, *el paso* literally means *step*, but it can also mean a crossroads.

I asked the girl if she wanted to meet up for a weekend there.

Maybe, she said.

*

Other customers in the El Paso Bar start to realize that Godzilla isn't just some weirdo in a costume. They try to buy him drinks, and they try to get him to pose for selfies. Godzilla bristles and brushes them off. When someone pulls his tail, he lets out a muted version of his roar, and the entire bar turns to stare.

Maricela the bartender arrives, speaking in Spanish too fast for me to follow. I toss her the bar towel.

'Hey,' I say to Godzilla. 'Want to get out of here?'

It's dark outside, and the air is cool. In California, no matter how hot it is during the day, it's always cold when the sun goes down. There's not much foot traffic here, and nobody pays us any mind. Godzilla plods, his fat tail sweeping the sidewalk behind us. He's cumbersome on the concrete, but as soon as we hit sand, he's agile, and I struggle to keep up.

'Have you ever been night swimming?' I ask.

'Is that a thing?' says Godzilla.

I shrug. 'I've never been.'

'Well, then,' he says. 'Let's go.'

My feet sink in the sand. Godzilla reaches the water's edge before me, but he waits. In the distance, specks of light from oil rigs twinkle on the horizon.

I'm suddenly embarrassed. Godzilla doesn't have any clothes to take off. I kick off my shoes and peel off my socks and wait until a cloud covers the moon, then I pull off my shirt and jeans.

Godzilla isn't interested in my body or its imperfections. The water is cold but calm, and waves lap the shore, regular as a heartbeat. Godzilla doesn't hesitate, just walks in a straight line into the sea. I splash up to my knees.

Godzilla is ahead, the water almost up to that big barrelled chest. Why is it so hard to walk in water but so easy to swim? Something to do with resistance. I charge through the surf until I'm waist deep, then I dive in. The water feels wonderful rushing around my face and neck, rolling down my back. Because it's salt water, I don't have to do much to stay afloat. I paddle to Godzilla, who is now neck-deep. I can no longer touch the bottom. I'm a strong swimmer, but I'm nervous. In the darkness, every tug of the water is amplified.

'Do you have to go back to Monster Island tonight?'

The moon emerges from the clouds, revealing Godzilla's face, but I still can't make out his expression. Its expression? Their expression.

'It's not a good idea for me to stay in any one place for too long.'

I think about all the possible lives under the sea. Rays rustling on the ocean floor, squid spiralling through the depths, whales singing their calves to sleep. When some species of whales sleep, they hang just under the surface, vertically, like stalactites. Other species continue to swim drowsily, nestled next to each other in pairs or pods. From time to time some hard-wired instinct propels them to the surface so they remember to breathe.

At night, coral unfold their tiny tentacles to grasp at drifting plankton. Starfish sweep the seabed for prey. Shrimp and krill rise from the depths to feed, ascending thousands of feet in enormous clouds. Fish, lacking eyelids, sleep with their eyes open, and sea otters hold hands to keep from drifting apart. At night, jellyfish pulse more slowly, and octopuses curl into their dens to dream. We've all seen that viral video of an octopus dreaming, her mantle pulsing from white to freckled brown to pale yellow, her skin contracting from smooth to rough, riddled with ridges, her whole body suddenly blushing violet. What do octopuses dream about?

Something slippery brushes against my leg, and I shriek. It's seaweed. Godzilla laughs.

I splash Godzilla, and they spit a stream of water at me. For a few minutes we play like children, laughing, swimming in bursts, churning the water, doing somersaults.

There are so many things I want to ask them, but it takes me a minute to catch my breath.

'Do you feel like a monster,' I blurt, 'or do we seem like the monsters to you?'

Godzilla's jaw bobs in the waves. 'Deep down, we're all monsters.' They turn to meet my gaze. I must have looked confused. 'We frighten each other. Hell, we scare ourselves.'

We're past the waves, but a surge of water lifts me a few inches then drops me. 'Have you ever been in love?' Underwater, Godzilla's tail curls around my ankle. I wriggle and kick, but I can't shake it off. 'Is it possible to fall in love when no other creature like you exists?'

Godzilla sighs and releases my ankle.

'Maybe.' They twist their mouth into what might be a smile before they duck under. I float, drifting with the current, waiting for Godzilla to resurface. Clouds cover the moon again. In the darkness, nothing separates the sea and sky. I can hardly make out where my skin ends and the sea begins.

I wait a long time. Then I remember that Godzilla doesn't actually swim. They simply walk along the ocean floor. I picture Godzilla walking home, plodding through the depths, engulfed in darkness, guided by instinct over underwater plains, past underwater hills, through underwater valleys, over sulphurous trenches, illuminated by the glow of bioluminescent worms.

Does Godzilla ever hover over a smoking fissure, the heat rippling the skin on their outstretched hand, and wonder, what would happen if they took another step? If they destroyed themselves, would they be reborn?

I float until my fingers and toes grow numb. I wonder what octopuses dream about, or if they dream at all. They think with their arms as much as their brains. I move my arms and legs, clumsy at first, then harder and faster as my muscles warm. I wonder if there is a shark nearby, tracing the electrical pulse of my heart. I picture a Portuguese man o' war, trailing tentacles a hundred feet long. Maybe I am already caught in an invisible rip tide that will sweep me out to sea.

When I grow tired of imaginary threats, I turn and head towards the shore. *Maybe*, I think, as all my possible lives splash and kick and sputter and rise and slosh naked through the shallow surf and into the cold night air. *Maybe, maybe, maybe.*

Allan Radcliffe
MEET FOR FUN

It's been months since I lifted my head and had a good look at this city. Princes Street's a mouth full of broken teeth. Waterstones isn't Waterstones any more. Burger King's gone too, replaced in its slot by an Apple Store that's lit up white inside.

At least the weather's familiar. The wind lifts the tufties on Sammy's head. He puts out his arms like bat-wings, makes giant steps towards the pedestrian crossing and watches a tram rounding the corner from St Andrew Square, big-eyed.

'You been on one, yet?' he asks, looking at me funny when I say no.

He begs and pleads and so we end up running for the stop, fumbling for coins then gliding along to Shandwick Place. I move near to his shoulder and breathe in while he gazes out. He's all cola and cake, a big kid.

*

We walk back under shop awnings. Sammy suggests an American-style restaurant that he remembers on Elm Row so we take a left, heading downhill.

'We went there for my birthday once. The waiters brought out a cupcake with a sparkler on it and my mum had a coronary because she thought they were going to charge extra.' He scans the signs. 'Could've sworn it was around here somewhere.'

We decide his restaurant has been replaced by a glitter-fronted café-bistro. We have to stand at the edge of the pavement to make out the name stretched along the sign. E-L-E-M-E-N-T.

It's empty save for a guy in regulation polo behind the counter. Hair shined to the squeak. I wonder for a moment how I know him, and then, as he takes shape, I remember a night in CC's, a trample over Calton Hill, a tenement stair. He was Rob or

Drew or Scott. He shouted his name over the music and I hadn't
caught it.

Table for two?

He was the first human I had touched since Frank. What slayed
was how quickly he unbuttoned my shirt using the fingers of one
hand. Afterwards he rolled a spliff and we passed it back and forth
until we were limp with laughter.

He's staring at me, his eyes narrowing in – what? Embarrassment?
But no, he's looking with friendly expectancy, as he would any
other passing trade.

Sammy grabs a table and we order spaghetti and drinks: a
half-carafe of red for me, which I downgrade to a large glass when
Sammy orders juice. I notice the appreciating look that Drew or
Jack or Scott gives Sammy when he collects our menus. What do
we look like to him, I wonder. A second date? A couple of old pals?

When I was out with Frank there was always attention. Nipping
to the shops would turn into a human obstacle course. Strangers
rubbernecked. I'd coorie in, possessive as hell. Later on, I could
almost enjoy the fact that so many people wanted him and he
was mine.

The furthest end of the window is a fresco of posters advertising
Polish–Scottish get-togethers and last year's festival shows. Sammy's
leaning forward with his palms resting on the table. For the first
time I get a look at his face square on. Heavy eyelids rise like a
garage door when he's in mid-flow.

'I like your hair,' he says. 'Very smart.'

'Not too drastic is it?'

'It's . . . *neat.*'

The first haircut in ages. I spent an hour traipsing Broughton
Street, gathering the nerve. The bell tinkled and straight away my
ears were bombarded with beats and chatter and hairdryers going.
Alison spotted me in the mirror over her client's head. *Gareth!*
She had a cancellation in twenty minutes if I didn't mind waiting.

The press of her fingers against my scalp was a narcotic. She spoke about her kids, her attempt to train for the half marathon, and then, partly to prevent a silence, partly to head off the question, I told her I'd been seeing someone.

'It's nothing: an old school friend. He's up here visiting family. I mean, he's in London most of the time and I'm up here. It's nothing.'

'That's a shame.' She peered at me. 'Right?'

'I mean, it's been fun, he's nice, but . . .'

And we both shrugged and swapped these little smiles, pretending lightness.

*

Rob or Scott or Andrew lowers bread onto the table. Sammy asks me if I've seen this or that film, expressing his disapproval when I admit I haven't even heard of any of them. He runs me through the plot of the new Tarantino, rounding off with a heartfelt thumbs down.

I watch his mouth. He's a talker, like Frank: he keeps on and on for fear some ghoul will creep in with the silence and steal his soul.

'How was your trip north?'

'My mum seems well enough. She made stew, which is a sure sign of a special occasion. Your dad . . .?'

'He lives in Portrush now. Northern Ireland. He and his wife spend their every waking minute on the golf course.'

My father sent a card when Frank died, with butterflies on the front and deepest sympathies inside. He phoned to say he was sorry but he couldn't make the funeral. He and Lucille were going on one of their cruises and they'd lose their deposit if they cancelled.

'I liked Frank,' he said. 'You know how I liked him, Gareth, but this trip's been booked months. It's not an easy matter for Lucille to get time off work.'

'Okay Dad, another time.'

We might have been rearranging a quick pint.

On the other side of the table Sammy takes a swig of juice, too fast, and an ice-cube collides with his teeth. I scrabble for his napkin. He puts a hand over mine, and for a few moments, before Rob or Jack or Scott appears with the spaghetti, we stay like that, holding hands in full view of the street, not saying anything, just staring off.

*

I've forgotten how this is meant to work. Romance. Not that I'm looking. This is strictly fun. That's what I put as my legend online: *meet for fun?* I want Sammy's fun. I want him to fun me.

With Frank it was different. He used to come into the café I worked in back when it was called Ground Up and we had a cassette player behind the counter. He and his friends would sit at the table by the window and order coffees and soup every day without fail.

I didn't pay all that much attention at first but one day, as I worked, I caught him looking past his friends, finding my eyes. I noticed his height and that military way he carried himself with his shoulders back and his chin out.

We played pool in the New Town bar that night. Five games, best of five, and I won every one of them. I cleaned up at darts too. Frank had no sense of aim. He threw his arrows across the table in mock disgust.

We went back to his flat in the West Port. There was music, some kind of jazz. I sat hugging one of the cushions off the sofa while I listened to him chunter on about Chet Baker who jumped out of a window and Billie Holiday, arrested on her deathbed for possessing heroin. Loving the nearness of him: it made me suddenly aware of every bit of my own body.

*

The fenced-off area outside CC's is full of fleecy hoods bobbing about with smoke streaming out the front of them. Two young guys go past, hand in hand. It was at this exact spot, a handful of years back, where Frank and I found ourselves caught up in the aftermath of a bashing and ended up in A&E with some poor fucker with cracked ribs. Frank had stepped in without hesitation. It's what he did. He would wade into other people's fights, right their wrongs then leave again, like the littlest hobo or some passing angel of mercy.

I don't think we ever held hands in the street, Frank and me. We wouldn't have lasted five seconds.

We turn onto Picardy Place and squeeze between the bouncers at the entrance to The Street. For some reason I expected Sammy to hesitate but he brightens as soon as we walk through the door. He pulls himself straight. He struts. He's home!

I catch sight of us in the mirror behind the bar: me in my pink shirt with my haircut that makes me look like my head's been sharpened; him in his denim jacket, the hood of his jumper exploding out the back. We are a pair.

'Is it me or is everyone in here twelve?' says Sammy.

I glance over at a table-full of cheek-boned humans, gazing down at their phones. I can barely remember being that age, the weightlessness of it.

The door swings behind us and another group blows in. They shift around then push towards the bar, the men clinging to the women for safety.

Sammy's twitching along to the music.

'I like her voice. Amy Winehouse.'

I don't have the heart to tell him this is Adele's 'Rolling in the Deep'.

'Look at them,' he says, nodding towards the crowd of newcomers. 'Refugees from a wedding reception. Imagine that lot in a place like this ten years ago.'

'I was sixteen the first time I went up Rose Street,' I say. 'Sat in the bus stop for half an hour before I went through the door, terrified someone might see me. I got to the bar and panicked and ordered a glass of wine.'

Sammy's giving me this funny, sad smile.

'Imagine if we'd known, all those years ago. School. All that. We could have been friends. We might have looked out for each other.'

*

We didn't immediately make the connection. Sammy and me. It came after the clean-up, the mortification. Dressed, I hovered at the end of the bed in his soulless hotel room with my hands clasped, more self-conscious with my clothes on than when we were both scuddy.

He had squirmed into a sitting position.

'You were at the Academy, weren't you?'

In the moment after he asked, I wondered if I should just lie.

'Knew I knew you from somewhere. You're Gareth Lockin.' He thumbed at his chest. 'I was Sammy Grieve. Year below but we had a couple of classes together. Biology. Third and fourth year. Mrs Petrie.'

'Petri Dish? There was a horror story.'

I looked at his face, trying to remould it, make it take on a younger shape, looking for something of our shared past in all those jutting bones.

He pulled the covers up over his chest, which I took as a signal for me to leave, but his mouth kept talking, filling the air with place names and names of teachers and kids whose faces had gone blank with time, and all this blather because a kind of adolescent shyness had crept between us. It was the mention of school that did it.

The only way to keep the silence at bay was to dig out our phones and go through the pantomime of swapping numbers.

'Yeah, let's keep in touch,' he said, punching at the screen. 'I'm not looking for a relationship or anything.'

'Me neither.'

He at least had the good grace to smile.

*

The bell goes for last orders and we join the convoy heading over to CC's.

Sammy looks put out at the thought of us cutting our losses. 'Come on then,' I say, wheeling him to the back of the line.

'This used to be a pit,' he says when we're inside. 'You could eat your tea off that floor now.'

The basement's a sauna. I keep my hand touched to Sammy's back as we push through the crowd. Faces I recognise, everywhere. I don't feel like speaking to any of Frank's friends. What I want is to dance and small-talk with Sammy until the lights go up and we all get to laugh at the state of each other's sweat-filled hair.

We perch among coats and jumpers. The DJ's playing this weird mash-up of Piaf and Gaga. We watch the dancers and Sammy kills himself at the sight of this kid in an oversized shirt locking and popping at the centre of a circle of admiring friends.

Sammy nods at the boy. 'If I didn't feel like an old toot before . . .'

'There was a time when I knew the name of every person in this place.'

Lights flash in diagonals across bodies. I head for the bar, engulfed in a sweet-smelling cloud that's hissing out from somewhere on the other side of the dance floor. A queen with a real brick of a jaw smiles and bows his head and make this big theatrical show of letting me pass, sweeping his arms before me like I'm *the* Queen and he's one of my courtiers. I turn and offer my most regal smile.

When I get back, Sammy points out a couple of smart-casual guys sitting on the other side of the dance floor. They're waving, making enquiring gestures.

'Oh, that's . . . Friends.' I tell Sammy. 'They're friends of my . . . Frank, you know. *Were.*'

I raise a hand and give them what I hope looks like my best-natured grin. Then I pretend they're not there, angle myself so I can watch Sammy, his eyes bouncing off the heads of the dancers.

I loved looking at Frank when he didn't know I was there. I loved him in profile, unawares. He was longsighted, and without his glasses he would hold whatever he was reading at arm's length. I loved looking at him from behind, loved the bits of him he couldn't see: the crown of his head with the ha'penny bald spot that never seemed to get any bigger, the nape of his neck. A label might be sticking out of his collar and the sight of it would undo me.

Sammy will leave in a couple of days, and then what? Some part of me wants his leaving to come sooner so we get out from under it – all that hugging and making sure we've got each other's numbers. That's no fun.

'Come on,' I say. 'Time to dance.'

He sticks up his hands in protest, but I manage to drag him onto the floor.

And, oh my God, he cannot dance. I grab him around the waist, trying to bend him into the right groove, but he seems in the zone, so I let him be.

Madonna comes on, 'Papa Don't Preach', and the floor fills. Sammy tips his head back, shakes out what he imagines is left of his hair.

*

'It's a while since I moved like that,' he says.

We keep going, turning at Pilrig Church. At some point Sammy notices that I'm away in my own head and only half-listening.

'You know . . . I wish . . .'

He doesn't say what he wishes.

'You're a lucky boy,' I say after a moment. 'You get to go back to London day after tomorrow. London, for fuck's sake. I'm jealous.'

'No, you're right,' he says, his voice flat. 'I mean . . . It was nice to meet up again.'

'It's been a laugh, hasn't it? It's been fun.'

'Right. I mean . . . I'll remember this.'

I can feel him, warm and expectant beside me. As we move down the road I find myself telling him that I'm thinking of taking a trip myself, to Portrush to see my father. It was half a thought until now. Saying it makes it more likely I'll actually go.

'How long will you be away?'

'Knowing my dad, not long.'

He reaches for me, just misses as I take a sudden totter over a loose slab. I turn, meaning to connect, but at that moment there's a shout from somewhere off to our right, a clatter of cans. A crowd of teens clustered inside the entrance to the park. One of the boys is enacting a drama, his arms waving around his head.

As I watch, the boy swivels in our direction. Slowly, as though a signal has sounded, his pals follow his gaze, until the whole group is facing us.

'Christ, it's like that scene out of *The Birds*,' Sammy says.

You two stab each other's arses?

'Let's go, Sammy,' I say.

A couple of the kids break loose from the pack.

'Come on, Sammy. Please.'

He takes my hand. 'They don't own the road, Gareth.'

His voice is as firm as his grip.

Arse-stabbers!

Their hilarity pursues us down the street, but they don't come any closer. We walk together, hand-in-hand, at a regal pace.

*

After our first time in the insipid hotel room I went home and lay in bed and thought about him. Sammy. He was losing his hair, receding in an attractive way. His woody aftershave clung to me after I left.

The thought of his face was soothing, like those scenic photos that bob up when the computer screen goes blank.

I had his number in my phone. If I wanted, I could get in touch with him. If I wanted to see him again I knew where to find him.

I rolled onto my side. Lay there for a while, pretending to be a different person. Bold. Wondering what I'd say, how I'd put it.

Hi Sammy, it was great to meet up with you . . .

Nice to see you the other day, Sammy . . .

Are you maybe free sometime to . . .?

If you're free sometime maybe we could . . .?

Maybe, if you're free . . .?

Maybe we . . .

The word repeated in my head over and over as sleep pulled me down.

Maybe

Maybe

Maybe

Mark Russell
TABULA RASA

The room has been emptied for decorating.
White paint, wooden floor and window frames,
sun bursting through summer's open doors,
a single chair for me to sit and read.

Next door takes the chance to mow the lawn;
rose and salvia stretch and yawn, posturing;
a buzz of far-off traffic settles beneath
birdcall in the ripe mountain's steep slumber.

Just when I think there's nothing, nothing
floods the space, pregnant, brisk, swarming.

Colin Scott
EMPTY NEST

the hoose wis empty a year
    afore we muived in
and it seemt it –
    the gairden hid gaun native

we clipped the gress
    hauf weeds onywey
an whiles we re-cut whit wis left o the beds
    we funn the wasp-bink

gane unnergrund they haed taen ower
    some ither sairy craitur's burrae
an A coud only imagine whit they haed buildit thare
    as we watched the wirkers dairt and drift

throu the dairk portal juist so wide
    fir ae baw – or ae wee dug's snout
which didnae bare thocht on
    but the landlord kept bees and wisna fasht

A could deal wi it masel or he wad
    wi a petrol-soaked cloot he said
rammed intae the hole
    he had a bee suit, so A thocht that best

twa nichts later he was pouin
    a white cotton coverall ower his street claes
likent tae a diver's dry suit
    the wey the mesh-kivert hood

flipped ower his heid front tae back
    and the zip ran shouther tae shouther
athort the back o his neck
    sealed and gloved he plunged intae the unner-growthe

the stink o petrol hung for oors efter he left
    straiglers came and went
back and forth in dribs and dregs
    aboot the wee bit scrappy cloot

blocking them from their hame and filling it
    wi noxious suffocating fumes
and by the morn's morn
    the colony wis deid

D. Hugh Taylor
EX TRAUMATA

After the unsuccessful little bomb
And on the very edge of feeling like it was too late
And the pure undignified stampede down the platform,
A flame I saw, but didn't look at it, made my eyeballs gold
Shit, shit, shit
Sanctuary became a sudden, remembered feeling,
An urgent word that surged forward into something almost past.

Scratching down a sandy track in summer
The sea, the constant sea, and the boat launch, nearby
With Archie's red hens tumbling from the marram grass
The sway of barley slowly blowing in the late afternoon sun
And sand martins ticking the air like punctuation.
Just sunlight and hirundine chatter
Ricocheting over Conieglen Water.

John White

TRAVELLING ACROSS BORDERS

(reading 'The Good Thief' from Tom Leonard's Six Glasgow Poems)

A brave journey, this boy
who picks his way through Catholic streets
haunted by the dark grotesque
of crucifixion.

Swerving the hard heads
of Glasgow's masculine tribes, his voice,
loving, sad, dry, comes alive in a time
we could throw words in the air.

For him language is bus-stop, hearth,
and bar. He turns the words of Glasgow
out to face the world. Away
from the academy that has nothing to say

about speech that gives the time of day
to the street. He leaves academy, reads
poems of self-deprecating, pared-down
troubled joy. Returns later

on his own terms. Lifts learning
out of learning, lays it on the same line
as patois spinning drunk with life
in the eleven p.m. launderette –

all sacred speech, all words
that turn on struggle, getting by, half-hidden
in the sideways banter of the day,
angry at the hypocrisies of class.

See Tom, I'm telling the people a story –
me the English boy from Surrey,
who used to get high
listening to you, Tom McGrath, Alan Spence

speaking up on stages,
or with the Other People crawling on the floor,
or sometimes see you wandering
in and out Tom's Bank Street kitchen,

me green and shy, skitting over the land,
too scared to stay. I'm telling a story
Tom, and you no longer here
to tell me I'm wrong.

Kirsti Wishart
SATELLITE OF LOVE

People are always surprised when Isobel tells them satellites don't come off production lines. Instead they are carefully handcrafted, precision-tooled scientific devices, each as individual as a work of art. She knows this because she makes them and remembers every one intimately, thinking of them as fondly as others do the cars they've owned. She imagines she feels the same way as painters do about their paintings, novelists their novels: pieces of herself, out there, reaching beyond her, affecting people's lives in ways she's too modest to admit to.

Times are changing, however. New firms have formed that allow for more generic machines, produced quickly, providing basic functions. There had been talk of job losses at her place of work and as she was close to retirement anyway, she opted for voluntary redundancy.

Working on the last craft she will ever complete, she grows more daring in her approach. Special, secret features she'd never dreamt of risking previously are built in like hidden code. To mark the twentieth anniversary of being with her girlfriend, Sarah, she interlaced their initials into components, imprinted the title of their favourite song – 'There Is A Light That Never Goes Out' – on a protective sheet of gold plate, added the curving form of a seahorse to the end of an antenna. This matches the tattoo curling underneath Sarah's earlobe as closely as the pulse of a warning light that hits the pace of Sarah's excited heartbeat.

Each of these additions Isobel can entirely justify from a technical point of view, yet space engineers are a surprisingly romantic bunch. She suspects she'd be allowed to get away with them if she confessed to her bosses. She prefers not to, having grown used to hiding parts of her life from others.

The night after the launch, she and Sarah treat themselves to a luxury hotel and a taxi ride to the Galloway Forest, a designated Dark Place where the glow from towns and cities won't cloud the stars. They are blessed in November with a spectacularly clear night and head with their torches leading the way along paths through the trees, rucksacks chinking with bottles of champagne, until they find themselves in a clearing alone.

It's as if some barrier, an earthly cataract has been removed, the heavens shining in super HD. Sarah is amazed by the spectacle: a thousand silvers, coppers and golds too, planets flickering blue and red, the shimmering blur of the Milky Way, the streak of falling space debris. 'Like frozen fireworks,' she murmurs.

There's a weird sense of vertigo gazing up, and although, clutching on to Sarah, Isobel tells her it's the alcohol making her dizzy, really it's the sense of the immense, being confronted by the genuinely sublime, beautiful and terrifying both. How tiny they are and yet with a brain created purely by chance, big enough to wonder at it.

Suddenly Isobel remembers and laughingly confesses to the side project she undertook as part of her PhD, probably hidden up in the attic somewhere. An orrery with the planets renamed to match partners and exes and friends. Turn the handle and women are drawn together by physical attraction, forced apart by jealousy and resentment, revolving and returning through the cooling bonds of friendship. A miniature solar system powered by love.

'You are *such* a lesbian!' Sarah teases, 'turning that sort of thing into a bit of engineering. It's like a Lego version of what's in a little black book. You'll have to get me added, a big moon orbiting planet Isobel.'

Isobel joins in her laughter, doesn't tell Sarah that when she was younger, before the days of sex being a touch-screen away, finding someone who would want her back felt as miraculous as witnessing a shooting star, a once-in-a-lifetime cosmic event. Instead she hugs her partner tight.

Isobel is of an age where taking hold of Sarah's hand in public still starts with a hesitation. She tries to feel glad when she sees younger gay couples walking down the street hand-in-hand, carefree, but there's always an undercurrent of envy; a quick, protective search on their behalf for any sign of disapproval from passers-by. Here, under cover of darkness, she can pull Sarah close, kiss without fear and can't help remembering the night kids shoved fireworks through their letterbox or when she was cornered in a pub by a drunk woman calling her a 'disgusting dyke' because of her short hair, visiting a friend in hospital who'd been beaten up for kissing his boyfriend at a bus-stop. She knows things are far better than they were. Lately though she's felt the darkness there at the fringes, lurking. She's under no illusion it could swallow them up unless the beacons are maintained, kept lit.

When she points out her satellite at midnight, she sets The Smiths playing from her phone – 'Look, there it is! I made it twinkle pink and lavender! 'cos I'm *such* a lesbian!' When she sees the wonder and pride in her girlfriend's gaze, she feels the burn of tears and can't decide entirely what they're for. There's joy in her achievement, yes, pain and worry too. Of giving up a job she loved, the uncertainty ahead, a black hole on the horizon. The concern that a lump, similar to the benign one she had removed from her breast the year before, might return, this time as hard and deadly as a tiny meteorite.

Sarah notices, lifts Isobel's clasped hand to her mouth, kisses each finger lightly. She whispers, breath sweet from champagne bubbles, 'These touched, *made* something up there. Amazing. Like an angel . . . a drunken angel.'

The satellite will help predict the weather, forecast heatwaves and typhoons, blizzards in April. It won't tell Isobel where she and Sarah will be in five, ten years' time. Whether they'll be together, secure in each other's gravity, or flung apart by forces unknown. She feels a refreshing sweep of not caring. Whatever happens there'll be the comfort of knowing that long after she and Sarah are dead and gone, the planet wrecked by a waiting catastrophe, above it queer space-junk will be floating. Carrying the best of her, signs of a warm heart in a freezing void, gleaming with hope, there for whoever's left to look up and make a wish, blinking in time to the pink and the lavender.

Bethany Wren
SHRIEK SONG

There is a girl. She lives under a green-tinged roof in the middle of nowhere. She lives on an island that was once inhabited by giants and witches, but now it is just humans and not so many of them as the girl lives far enough away from anyone else that she must walk for miles to get to the shop or to the pub.

Maybe there was once an old woman here who knew which herbs could heal a person and which ones would cause a slow and painful death. Maybe there used to be huge battles between the tribes and, if you listen closely on a quiet day, you can still hear the sounds of swords swinging through the air. Maybe the land under the girl's feet is saturated with the bones of her ancestors. She belongs to this earth and it belongs to her.

Maybe she's just a girl who lives under a green-tinged roof in the middle of nowhere.

She's not a girl, not really. She's at that in-between stage where everything she does seems to catch on the world around her. She lives with her father who works long hours and drinks long nights. Every day that passes means she is one day less a girl and one day more a woman. Time has been taking from her all the things she loves.

The girl trudges through the darkness every morning before school to sort the day's newspapers at the newsagent's in the village. It's a boring job. The dust from the back room causes her eyes to itch and her fingers are always blackened with ink. Old Billy pays her five euros a morning for her hard work, and although it's not much, it means that she doesn't have to go to her father every time she needs something, like new shoes or sanitary pads or dinner on the nights when he doesn't come home.

It's not been the same since her mother died, but they make do.

At school, the girl is quiet. Her classmates are boisterous and seem to be always frothing over with jokes and screeches. There is a loudness to them the girl doesn't know if she will ever find within herself. She doesn't even raise her hand in English, although it has always been her favourite subject. She reads everything she is told to – and more. The librarian allows her to take out more books than anyone else, the pages are bruised with her fingerprints.

Her teachers are asking them all about universities and apprenticeships, but the girl knows that she can't leave her father so she keeps her lips sealed tight when they ask her what she will do. It is better to be quiet. Better not to be noticed.

At night, the girl lies awake, listening to her father's snores in the next room and reflecting on the books she has read and the stories she has been told. She thinks of the women hanged in the village, the angry mob who drove them there, accused them of being witches. Of governesses and secret wives hidden in the attic. Wars taking place within a hundred pages, whole lives woven into paper. The stories of the people in the village and who – and what – they claim to have seen.

She has always found herself in the dark. The world is much softer when you can't see it. The girl can reach out her hand, stretching it into the blackness until it disappears, and then it doesn't exist anymore. And neither does she.

This is true freedom: to reinvent yourself every night. She is the author, casting herself into the lead roles and dreaming herself into someone else.

But there's something more – something she hasn't told anyone about. It festers within her chest, rising up to make her sick if she thinks about it too much. Now she reads late into the night, forcing her eyes across the pages until it is light outside so that when she finally falls asleep, exhausted, she is too tired to remember.

Because what are secrets if they are said aloud?

It concerns old Billy's grandson who sometimes works at the newsagent's in the morning, putting out stock, leaning over the counter and looking at her with eyes that have always wanted something. It concerns what took place one morning before school when Billy was out of town and it was just the two of them, the girl sorting the newspapers as fast as she could so she could leave and get to school.

It concerns shame. And pain. Crying in the toilet when she is supposed to be in class. Getting through the day to go home and find her father is already at the pub and has left a note saying to sort herself out for dinner. Closing the curtains and lying on the bed, squeezing her eyes hard to make it dark, and trying trying just for one moment to be more than herself.

She tucks the secret into the corners of her lips and promises herself she will never tell. Every morning she has gone back to the shop and prayed he won't be there. Time is passing and she is growing hollow with what she knows. There's a feeling at the pit of her stomach like an opening. It starts deep within her, working its way up to her mouth.

Before she knows it, it has nearly come out.

It's not words stuck in there – it's something else. But the girl is frightened, so she keeps it all in.

One night there is a storm. The skies wrench themselves open and rain drenches the land below. The wind roars, moving through the world in anger, tearing at trees and branches and lifting at roofs and structures, looking in, wanting to bring the inside out. The girl is home alone. She told her father not to go out drinking, but he grimaced at her and put on his heavy coat and boots and disappeared into the darkness without another word.

He's been doing that ever since her mother died: forgetting to use words, shuffling about the house with shaking fingers. A quietness has settled into their lives like a blanket of snow. They are muffled and frozen inside.

She can picture the pub now with its soft light and stench of male sweat and stale beer. At times like this, it will be packed, the village gathering together to seek comfort from what they can't control. Her father will be sitting at the bar with Conor and Danny.

Mark will be there, maybe Patrick too. Old Billy will be in the corner with Dec and Roger.

Maybe he will be there. Maybe he will be drinking with his friends who have all left school now, but don't seem to have anything to do apart from drink too much and stir up trouble. Old Billy will keep him in line if they are there together.

He won't be thinking of her, of that she's sure. She will never cross his mind for longer than it takes for him to catch her eye and smile with the knowledge of what he's done to her.

Inside, she burns.

As the storm picks up outside, she moves through their small house in a daze, picking up items and putting them back down again without really looking at them – her hairbrush, her homework, her mother's mirror and trinkets still left untouched, her father's ashtray, the TV remote.

The energy of the storm is running through her. It thrums under her chest and pulses through her skin. She thinks of him again and imagines striking him down with lightning, like some ancient goddess. It would be the only way to make him feel something, to make him understand. As she paces up and down the hallway, up and down the stairs, around and round her bedroom, she does not feel ashamed for wanting it.

She does not feel ashamed any more of what he did to her. She is filling up with the anger of it all.

When she finally stops, she can hear something outside. It's more than the storm. It's more than anything she's heard before. It's a part of the weather, but also separate. It echoes and calls back to the wind, crying out to the rain and howling at the clouds. She pauses, heart stopped still, because she knows what it is in an instant, even though she's never heard it before. She is a child of her people, after all.

They have all heard the stories about the wailing woman.

The banshee is a warning and a premonition. Her cry is to let the world know that somebody is about to die. It's the tolling of a bell. It's a lamentation, a keening for the loss of life. It's the sound that has haunted these shores since the beginning of time. It's the sound you hope you never hear.

The girl's mother told her all the stories about the times the banshee has been heard shrieking. She can list them like a prayer.

They heard her before the witch trials up the road, hundreds of years ago.

They heard her when the girl's great-great-aunt lost the baby in childbirth, and then she died as well.

They heard her the day the boys fell into the river and drowned before the girl was born.

Sometimes the banshee is too late, and all you can hear is a murmur on the wind at a deathbed. Some say that she is a wrinkled old woman, hunched over and stumbling. Some say that she is small, like a fairy, with eyes that glow red when she screams.

The sound from outside continues, getting louder now as the girl stands up, her heart beating fast. She always thought that she would be afraid, but now that it comes to it, she is not frightened. She is listening.

She is listening to the noise and it doesn't sound much like a scream – not really. It has tone and pitch. It undulates like a wave, rising and falling like a ship in the night. It is beautiful.

In her mind she can see their land rolling and rolling until there is nothing left and it drops off into the sea. She can see the rain, the essence of this place, feel the soil in between her fingers, sticky and smooth.

It's not a scream. No, it's a song. Why has nobody ever told her this before? She cannot be scared of something so full and vivid. It's moving within her.

Her mouth is opening of its own accord – she gulps in a breath and closes it again.

She wants to go outside and see it for herself. There's no time for a coat or shoes, so she rushes out barefoot, her school uniform blowing itself from her bones, her hair immediately wet and sticking to her face, running through the front garden to the gate, opening it with shaking fingers and then out into the road which is blustering and empty.

The girl feels the need to close her eyes. She closes her eyes and opens her mouth for the ancient sound that is making its way through her stomach and throat and now it is coming – full force – through her lips.

They hear it in the pub too.

What's that? calls someone and they all pause, drinks on the way to their mouths, a shiver of fear running up the spines of those old enough to remember the last time.

Jesus, says Danny, eyes wide. She's back.

The shriek, which began quietly, has grown in size. It pauses for a moment and they all look at each other, the stillness of the pub ringing, the storm screeching around them. And then the scream begins again and it takes them all a heartbeat to work out why it's louder this time. It's not closer. It's doubled in size.

There are two voices screaming.

The younger ones put their heads in their hands trying to cover their ears. What is it? they ask but nobody answers them because they all know what it is and they are all terrified.

The girl's father cocks his head from the bar.

It can't be?

But he'd recognise that sound anywhere. He might be four pints down and he might never be around long enough to listen to his daughter's voice, but he would know that scream if he were at the bottom of the deepest ocean and she were at the top of the highest mountain.

Fiadh, he calls her name and everyone has stopped looking at each other in fear and are now looking at him in fear.

When Fiadh opens her eyes, she is still making that noise and somehow it is matching and going against the other voice in some kind of unearthly harmony. The banshee is here and in front of her now and for one moment the long, dark hair and wide, green eyes make her think it is her mother – but then she steps closer and can see that it's not.

The woman is no crone. She is ageless because she does not exist in this time. Her hair flows behind her in the wind but it is not wet. Her face is smooth and pale, her lips open as still she sings, her cloak straight and simple, her palms open. She could be any one of them.

When the woman reaches Fiadh, something tells her to stop making that noise and so she does, and the woman does too. They look at one another, Fiadh squinting through the dark. The wind picks up a tile from the roof and drops it on the ground so that it shatters dully in the distance.

Fiadh holds the woman's gaze, unable to look away. She looks as if she wants to say something. Her eyes widen with a meaning that Fiadh can't grasp, although she desperately wants to understand her.

There is something between them that can't be expressed, not through words.

They stand in this way for what feels like hours, Fiadh no longer feeling the cold and the wet. She wants more than anything to stay here forever, to hold this moment – and this song – in her heart. Maybe to follow the woman back to where she came from. She has lost all sense of time and place, of being human and standing in the middle of a storm. All she can do is look at this creature who looks a little bit like her mother and a little bit like her.

Finally, Fiadh steps forward so that there is no more distance between them. The woman watches her with eyes that hold a thousand stories. Slowly, Fiadh lifts her arm and reaches out towards her. Their gazes are locked and Fiadh can hear the music of the storm around her (how could she never hear this as music before?) as she takes the woman's hand into her own.

It doesn't feel like skin. It's a pocket of air in the shape of a hand, like trying to grasp the wind itself. But Fiadh can feel something in the touch – a lick of flames that matches the fire within her own heart. A burning that they share.

The woman tightens her ghostly fingers around Fiadh's and, finally, she understands.

It's knowing that she's nothing more than a seed in this land and she will grow both down into the ground and up into the sky.

It's an instinct ingrained somewhere deep within her. A strength she didn't know she had.

It's a pain deep within her belly, not unlike what she has experienced before. It's felt by all those who are wronged and those who must bleed.

It's a wailing. For what she must face in order to become who she is.

She looks at the woman until she cannot look at her any longer and she must close her eyes, must raise her head to the sky and let the rain wash down her face, must open her lips and let that sound come out again. It is the only way to let go.

They sing together. They let the storm guide the notes, tell them where to go high and low, when to go softly softly quiet and when to roar from the pits of their stomachs like they are wild animals. They are still holding hands. They sing the shriek song together and when Fiadh finally opens her eyes, she realises that the woman is gone, she is holding nothing and that she is singing by herself, the noise moving through the land and towards her father who is running to her as fast as he can.

But it's too late. The rain is growing heavier, lashing at Fiadh who stands alone in the storm, eyes fixed on the empty space before her, fingers clenching and unclenching by her side.

She belongs to this earth and it belongs to her.

She is waiting for the lightning to strike.

BIOGRAPHIES

Craig Aitchison has an MLitt in Creative Writing from Stirling University. His poetry features in *Poetry Scotland* and on the Scottish Poetry Library website. He has had fiction published by Crowvus Press, *Fictive Dream*, *Northwords Now*, *Southlight* and *Pushing Out the Boat*. He won the 2021 Sangschaw prize for fiction.

Juliet Antill lives on the Isle of Mull. Her poems have appeared most recently in *Magma*, *The Dark Horse*, *Poetry Scotland* and *Northwords Now*.

Jane Archer's work is published in a variety of national anthologies, including *Unbound New Writing* and *Gutter*. She is currently Associate Artist (Writer) with Horsecross Arts and Mindspace, delivering 'My Life, My Story' and 'My Life, My Stage' creative writing workshops. She is also a freelance project worker for Autumn Voices where she supports older people in Perthshire to tell their story.

Peter Bennett is from Tollcross, Glasgow. He left school at fifteen and worked in a variety of jobs before returning to education, studying at Paisley University. Following that, he worked in construction, eventually retraining as a health and safety advisor. His debut novel, *Liberties*, from which 'Stovies' is extracted, is to be published by Rymour Books later this year. He lives with his wife and children in East Kilbride.

Karen Elizabeth Bishop is a UK/US poet, translator, and scholar. Brought up along the Moray Firth and in Southern California, she now teaches literature at Rutgers University. Her debut poetry collection, *the deering hour*, was published in 2021 by Ornithopter Press.

Nathan Breakenridge is a writer based in Edinburgh. He attended the University of Stirling Creative Writing MLitt program, and has previously had his work published in the likes of *Gutter*, *Neon*, *Pushing Out the Boat*, and *Not Deer*, among others. In 2019, he was shortlisted for the Scottish Book Trust New Writers Award.

Niki Brennan is a writer and poet from Glasgow. He was the first-prize winner of the Federation of Writers' 2021 Vernal Equinox poetry competition and was previously shortlisted for the Bridport Fiction Prize. His work has appeared in *Gutter*, *Crow & Cross Keys* and *Wrongdoing* magazine, amongst others.

Mikey Burnett is an Edinburgh playwright and screenwriter who writes predominantly in the east-coast vernacular. His most recent play, *The Bookies*, co-written with Joseph McCann, premiered with Dundee Rep in May 2022. His short film, *In Her Corner*, is in post-production, and he is currently developing his Scots language adaptation of Shaw's classic, *Pygmalion*.

Emily Christie is a writer living in Dundee. Her work has been featured in *The Wee Review*, *Marbles Mag* and *Potluck Zine*. Emily loves reading and writing about all things macabre and when not pretending to be a gothic heroine enjoys watching every film ever released and being too competitive at boardgames.

Kate Coffey is a Brighton-based writer with an interest in folklore and myth. She has been published previously in *New Writing Scotland* 39 and *Mslexia*, and was shortlisted for the Bath Short Story Award 2020.

Lynn Davidson's latest poetry collection *Islander* was published by Shearsman Books, Bristol, and Victoria University Press, Wellington, in 2019. Lynn had a Hawthornden Fellowship in 2013 and a Bothy Project Residency in 2016. She won the 2020

Poetry New Zealand Poetry Award, and was 2021 Randell Cottage Creative New Zealand Writer in Residence.

Lil DeThomas is a genderfluid poet, musician, and artist from Denver, Colorado. Their work has been featured in *Periphery Art and Literary Journal*, *Tenth Street Miscellany*, *86 Logic*, and now *New Writing Scotland*. They worked as a burrito artist for five years, and consequently, can roll a burrito the exact shape and size of a beer can.

Shehzar Doja is Founder/Editor-in-Chief of *The Luxembourg Review* and Poetry Reviews Editor at *Gutter*. His poetry and translations have appeared in *New Welsh Review*, *Poetry Wales*, *Pratik*, *Modern Poetry in Translation*, *Voice and Verses*, *Ceremony*, *Poems from the Edge of Extinction*, *Fundstücke-Trouvailles* and more. **shehzardoja.com**, Twitter **@shehzar**

Meg Eden is a 2020 Pitch Wars mentee, and teaches creative writing at Anne Arundel Community College. She is the author of the 2021 Towson Prize for Literature-winning poetry collection *Drowning in the Floating World* (Press 53, 2020) and children's novels, most recently *Selah's Guide to Normal* (Scholastic, 2023). **www.megedenbooks.com**, Twitter **@ConfusedNarwhal**, Instagram **@meden_author**.

Ellen Forkin is a chronically ill writer living in windswept Orkney. She has a love for all things folklore, myth and magic. Find her published and upcoming work in *The Haar*, *Paragraph Planet*, *Crow & Cross Keys* and in *Ghostlore* on the Alternative Stories podcast.

Timothy Fox is originally from Texas. He received a Houston Press Theatre Award for his play 'The Whale; or, Moby-Dick' and a Vault Festival Spirit Award for his play 'The Witch's Mark'. His poetry has appeared in numerous journals. He is a graduate of the Royal Conservatoire of Scotland. **www.timothy-fox.com**

Roshni Gallagher is a poet based in Edinburgh. She is a Scottish Book Trust New Writer's Awardee 2022. Her work can be found in *Gutter, Best Scottish Poems 2020, Butcher's Dog, Middleground,* and *The Scotsman*. In her work, she explores themes of nature, connection, and memory.

Rodge Glass is the author of three novels, two graphic novels, a collection of short stories and a literary biography of Alasdair Gray, which was the winner of a Somerset Maugham Award for nonfiction. His next book is *Michel Faber: The Writer and his Work* (Liverpool University Press, 2023).

Heather Gregg writes with paper, video, audio, artworks, curating multimedia exhibitions and is studying for a Masters in Intermediality: literature, film and the arts in dialogue. She is fascinated by creativity, communication, and collaborations between the arts. The Facebook page, **HeatherGreggCreative**, encourages other people's creativity and advertises her online workshops.

Kris Haddow is a playwright, poet, performer and author from Dumfries and Galloway who has won awards for Scots dialect writing. A University of Glasgow MLitt Creative Writing graduate, he is currently writing his first novel while researching Lallans and South West Scots representation in publishing in pursuit of their DFA. **www.krishaddow.com**, Twitter **@KrisHaddow**

Nat Hall is a Norman-born, Shetland-based poet and visual artist, co-author-translator of *From Shore to Shoormal* (2012), author of *Compass Head* (2016) and translator of Georges Dif's *Shetland* (2018). Published in *The New Shetlander, Poetry Scotland, Stravaig,*

Northwords Now and in several anthologies, she is currently working on her second collection.

Alan Hill was born in the UK and immigrated to Canada in 2005. He is the former Poet Laureate of the City of New Westminster, BC (2017–2020), former president of the Royal City Literary Arts Society (RCLAS), and was the editor and curator of *A Poetry of Place: Journeys Across New Westminster*, published in partnership with New Westminster Arts Services. His writing has been published both in Canada and internationally. His latest book, *In The Blood*, was published by Caitlin Press in 2022.

Alex Howard's poetry has appeared in *Aesthetica*, *Orbis* and *Gutter*, and his debut novel *Library Cat* (2016) won the People's Book Prize. His academic book, *Larkin's Travelling Spirit*, was published in 2021, and his latest novel is due out next year. He works as Creative Engagement Assistant at Capital Theatres, Edinburgh.

Shane Johnstone is a Glaswegian poet and author. His poems and prose, in Gaelic and Scots, have been published in *New Writing Scotland*, *Wet Grain*, *Lallans*, *Pushing Out the Boat* and *Product*, and his debut novel *The Gods of Frequency* was published in 2020 by Arkbound Publishing.

Charles Lang is from Castlemilk in Glasgow. He studied English Literature at the University of Edinburgh and is currently pursuing a PhD in Creative Writing at the Seamus Heaney Centre, Queen's University Belfast. His published work includes *Aye ok* (Speculative Books, 2020) and *As If* (Fallow Media, 2021).

Len Lukowski is a writer, poet and performer based in Glasgow. His work has been published in *The Quietus*, the *Huffington Post*, *Magma* and many other publications. His poetry pamphlet *The*

Bare Thing is published by Broken Sleep Books. He is the winner of the Wasafiri 2018 New Writing Award for Life Writing.

Aoife Lyall's debut poetry collection *Mother, Nature* (Bloodaxe Books, 2021) was shortlisted for the Scottish First Book Award 2021. The writing of her second collection was supported by the National Lottery through Creative Scotland. Lyall lives and works in the Highlands. She is currently writing her first novel.

Hannah McDonald is a writer and teacher from the Southside of Glasgow. Her work has been published in The Common Breath's *Middle of a Sentence*, *SPAM* zine and *Gutter*. You can follow her on Twitter @mcdonaldhanny.

Crìsdean MacIlleBhàin/Christopher Whyte will be publishing two new novels, *Beyond the Labyrinth* and *Towards Awakening*, with Cloud Machineries Press in October 2022. His eighth poetry collection, *Mo Shearmon / What I Have To Say*, in Gaelic with facing English translations, will be published in 2023 by Francis Boutle Publishers. A sixth book of translations from the Russian of Marina Tsvetaeva, *Head on a Gleaming Plate*, is to appear shortly with Shearsman Books. **www.christopherwhyte.com**

Liz McKibben is an Edinburgh bairn who grew up with a love of Scots and English. She studied German and French and is currently wrestling with Spanish. She enjoys transreading poems, including from endangered languages. Her work has been published in *New Writing Scotland* and *Northwards Now*.

Jane McKie's publications include the poetry pamphlet *From the Wonderbook of Would You Believe It* (Mariscat, 2016), and the collection *Quiet Woman, Stay* (Cinnamon Press, 2020). She won the Wigtown 2021 Prize Alastair Reid Pamphlet Competition for

Jawbreaker. Jane is a Senior Lecturer in Creative Writing at the University of Edinburgh.

Hugh McMillan's poetry has been published widely and he has won various prizes. In 2021 Luath published two collections: *Haphazardly in the Starless Night*, and *Whit If?*, poems about Scottish history. In 2021 he was chosen as the editor of the Scottish Poetry Library's anthology *Best Scottish Poems*. He edits for Drunk Muse Press. **www.hughmcmillanwriter.co.uk**

Scott McNee tutors in English and Creative Writing at the University of Strathclyde. His short fiction and poetry have been published in *Tether's End*, *Kalopsia*, *Gutter*, *Quotidian* and *The Grind*. He is currently working on a short story collection.

Caoimhin MacNèil/Kevin MacNeil is a writer from the Outer Hebrides, now resident in Stirling where he is a Lecturer in Creative Writing. His three novels include *The Brilliant & Forever*. He has edited books by Robert Louis Stevenson and Iain Crichton Smith. MacNeil has written for stage, radio, television, and cinema. He has read his work in Japan, Colombia, the USA, Sweden, and many other countries. **www.kevinmacneil.me**

Paul McQuade is an award-winning writer and translator from Glasgow, Scotland. He has received the Sceptre Prize for New Writing and the Austrian Cultural Forum Writing Prize. He is the co-author of *Hometown Tales: Glasgow*, and his debut short story collection, *Between Tongues*, was published by Cōnfingō in 2021.

Callum McSorley is an author based in Glasgow. His short stories have appeared in *New Writing Scotland*, *Gutter*, *Shoreline of Infinity*, *Monstrous Regiment*, and many more. His debut novel will be published by Pushkin Vertigo in 2023.

Andrea Mejía is a Mexican writer and translator residing in Scotland. She is a Creative Writing MSc graduate from the University of Edinburgh. She has published a novel in Spanish, *Los Sueños Más Oscuros* (*The Darkest Dreams*), and short stories with independent publishers in the UK and South Africa.

Claire O'Connor is an educator who has worked with students of many ages in New York, California, Idaho, Morocco, Malaysia, Greece, South Africa, and Scotland. Her stories have appeared in *The Baltimore Review*, the *Southern Indiana Review*, *Shenandoah*, *Wigleaf*, and others. She was a 2022 Best of the Net Finalist in Fiction, and she has previously won The Missouri Review's Miller Audio Prize for prose. She lives with her wife in Scotland and various other parts of the world.

Allan Radcliffe's short stories have been published widely and broadcast on BBC Radio 4, and he is a recipient of a Scottish Book Trust New Writer's Award. His first novel, *One Day All This Will Be Yours*, is due to be published in 2023 by Fairlight Books.

Mark Russell's full collections are *Shopping for Punks* (Hesterglock), and *Spearmint & Rescue* (Pindrop). He won the Magma Poetry Judge's Prize in 2020, and his poems have appeared recently in *Shearsman*, *Tears in the Fence*, *The Manchester Review*, *The Interpreter's House*, and *bath magg*.

Colin Scott: A've written aw ma life and published occasionally, maistly plays and some poetry tho writin in Scots is a new stairt for me. A've juist moved back to Ayrshire efter leevin in the Channel Islands fifteen year whaur A took pairt in mony public readings an ither leeterer events.

D. Hugh Taylor is an art historian and writer. His poetry is often based on various human responses to urban and natural landscapes, and the connections between the two, and on the effect of memory, mortality and desire on creating those responsive experiences.

John White was first published in Michael Horovitz's seminal review *New Departures*. He was a TV/New Media Director/Producer for some years. He graduated with Distinction from the Poetry School/Newcastle University Writing Poetry MA in 2021. He has a Covid lockdown performance poem online at **newbootsandpantisocracies**, and has poems recently in *The New European*, *The Alchemy Spoon*, and *The Ekphrastic Review*.

Kirsti Wishart's short stories have appeared in *New Writing Scotland*, *404 Ink*, *Glasgow Review of Books*, *The Seven Wonders of Scotland* anthology, *Product* and *Biopolis: Tales of Urban Biology*. Her first novel, *The Knitting Station*, appeared in March 2021 with *The Projectionist* following in February 2022. Come say hello **@kirstiw**.

Born in Hertfordshire and based in Edinburgh, **Bethany Wren** graduated from Royal Holloway, University of London's Creative Writing MA with a Distinction in 2020. She is currently finishing work on her novel and short story collections. Bethany can be found drinking coffee, enjoying life in Scotland, and on Twitter at **@beth_wren**.